REVISE EDEXCEL GCSE (9–1)

Mathematics

MODEL ANSWER WORKBOOK

Foundation

Series Consultant: Harry Smith

Author: Navtej Marwaha

Pearson

Contents

A small bit of small print:
Edexcel publishes Sample Assessment Material and the Specification on its website. This is the official content and this book should be used in conjunction with it. The questions and mark schemes have been written to help you practise every topic in the book. Remember: the real exam questions and mark schemes may not look like this.

About your exam

Your Edexcel (9–1) Mathematics GCSE comprises **three exam papers.**

Paper 1 | **Paper 2** | **Paper 3**

Each paper…

- is 1 hour 30 minutes
- is worth 80 marks
- is worth 33% of the total
- assesses all content areas
- progresses in demand

and will assess your skills and knowledge using a range of question types:

- structured questions, which break the task down into steps
- unstructured questions, which require you to structure your answer
- contextual questions, which make use of real-life situations.

Edexcel (9–1) Mathematics GCSE has two tiers. This book is for students planning to sit Foundation-tier exams.

Grades available at Foundation tier:

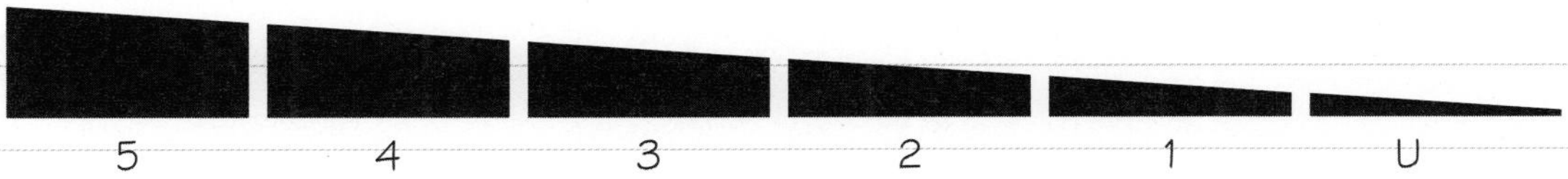

The chart below shows the percentage of marks available across the Foundation-tier exams for each content area.

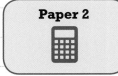

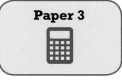

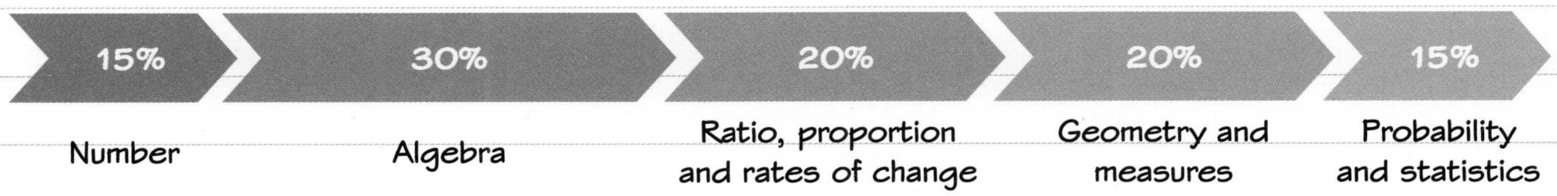

Mark schemes

Mark schemes tell you what the marker is looking for in your answer. Throughout this book, you will be introduced to using simplified mark schemes alongside exam-style answers. Here are some of the things to look out for.

These codes tell you what to award marks for:

Code	Meaning
M	Mark for correct or partly correct method
P	Mark for correct process or step in a problem-solving question
A	Mark for accuracy in using a method or process
C	Mark for clear communication, such as an accurate graph line
B	Mark for correct answer – no working needed
cao	Mark for the correct answer only
oe	'Or equivalent' – equivalent answers accepted

This question requires three processes, with one mark available for each. Even if you do not arrive at the correct answer, you can still gain marks for using the right approach.

The notes tell you how to award marks.

Answer	Notes
$x = 4$, $y = -0.5$	M1 for a correct method to eliminate one variable M1 for a correct method to find second variable A1 for $x = 4$, $y = -0.5$

The correct answer is given in the left column.

There is one accuracy mark available for the correct answer.

How to use this book

In this book, you will familiarise yourself with the Edexcel (9–1) Mathematics GCSE by engaging with exam-style questions, answers and mark schemes. Doing so means you will know exactly what to expect in the exam and, just as importantly, what will be expected of you.

Each activity type asks you to engage with an exam-style question in a different way. You can work your way from front to back or focus on pages that test the skills you need to improve.

Read the activity instructions carefully before you begin – it's good practice for the exams!

Mark schemes tell you what the marker is looking for. See page 2 for more information.

Real-life students have shared some of their tips and techniques for exam success.

Number

Mark the answer

1 Use the mark scheme to assign a mark to the answer.

Remember to find a common denominator before adding or subtracting fractions.

5 Work out $5\frac{3}{4}+\frac{7}{9}$

Give your answer as a mixed number in its simplest form.

(3 marks)

$5\frac{3}{4}+\frac{7}{9}=5+\frac{3}{4}+\frac{7}{9}$

$=5+\frac{27}{36}+\frac{28}{36}=5\frac{55}{36}$

$5\frac{55}{36}$

Answer	Notes
$6\frac{19}{36}$	M1 for converting both fractions to get a common denominator of a multiple of 36, with at least one of the fractions correctly converted. M1 (dep on M1) for $5+\frac{"27"}{36}+\frac{"28"}{36}\left(=5\frac{55}{36}\right)$ A1 cao

I would award the answer ...... out of 3 marks because ......

2 Use the mark scheme to assign a mark to the answer.

12 There are 75 students in a school. The school organises three trips. Each student can choose to go on one trip. They can go to a theme park, a castle or a zoo.

25 students choose the zoo.
40 students are girls.
15 girls choose the theme park.
17 boys choose the theme park.
Equal numbers of boys and girls choose the castle.

Complete the two-way table.

(3 marks)

When I fill in a two-way table, I always check all the totals in the table match the totals in the question.

	Theme park	Castle	Zoo	Total
Girls	15	8	17	40
Boys	17	8	10	35
Total	32	18	25	75

Answer	Notes
15, 9, 16, 40 17, 9, 9, 35 32, 18, 25, 75	B1 for 15, 17, 25, 40, 75 B1 for 32 or 35 or 18 B1 for all correct entries

I would award the answer ...... out of 3 marks because ......

6

Hints guide you in the right direction, from guidance on getting started to tools and methods that can help you find the answer.

This stamp tells you the level of the student answer on the page. There are three levels of answer: Had a go, Nearly there and Nailed it!

Student answers are always written in red.

Answers to activities are written in blue. You can find them in the back of the book, starting on page 76. Answers provided in blue will be examplar, which means they're examples of very strong answers.

Marker's comments tell you what an answer has done well and what could be done better.

Number

Improve the answer

1 Use the hint to write an improved answer that would be awarded 2 marks.

14 Tom goes to a restaurant.
He can choose from three types of burgers and three types of side dishes.

Tom is going to choose one burger and one side dish.

List all the possible combinations Tom can choose.

Burger	Side
Beef Veggie Chicken	Salad Fries Potatoes

(2 marks)

Hint
- Use letters for the options. For example, use B for 'beef'.

Nearly there

BS, BF, BP, VS, VF, VP, CS, CF, CP, SB, SV, SC, FB, FV, FC, PB, PV, PC

BS, BF, BP, VS, VF, VP, CS, CF, CP

The student has written too many combinations.

2 For each part of the question, write an improved answer that would be awarded full marks.

11 $A = 52000$ and $B = 3 \times 10^3$
Giving your answers in standard form, work out:

(a) $A + B$

(2 marks)

Hint
- To answer parts (a) and (b), work with ordinary numbers. Then, convert to standard form at the end.

Had a go

$5.2 \times 10^4 + 3 \times 10^3 = 8.2 \times 10^6$ ...... 8.2×10^6

$52000 + 3000 = 55000 = 5.5 \times 10^4$ ...... 5.5×10^4

(b) AB

(2 marks)

Nearly there

$5.2 \times 10^4 \times 3 \times 10^3 = 15.6 \times 10^7$ ...... 15.6×10^7

The student's final answer is not in standard form.

$5.2 \times 10^4 \times 3 \times 10^3 = 15.6 \times 10^7 = 1.56 \times 10^8$ ...... 1.56×10^8

3 Write an improved answer to each part of the question that would be awarded full marks.

4 Write the following numbers to the stated degree of accuracy.

(a) 0.07483 correct to three decimal places.

(1 mark)

Had a go

...... 0.0748 ...... 0.075

(b) 0.07483 correct to three significant figures.

(1 mark)

Had a go

...... 0.075 ...... 0.0748

The student has confused the meanings of 'decimal places' and 'significant figures'.

4

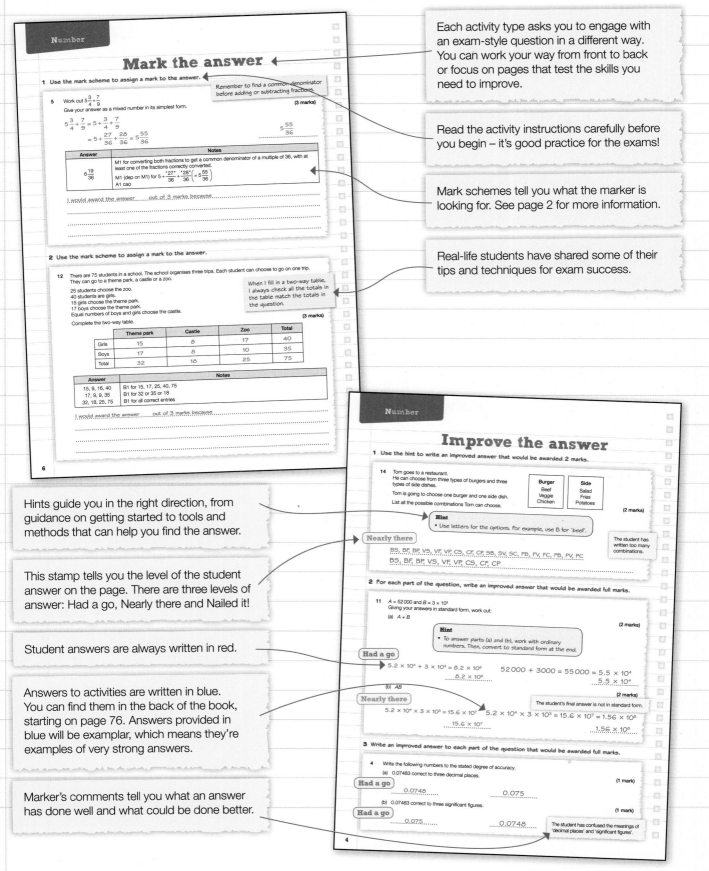

Improve the answer

1 Use the hint to write an improved answer that would be awarded 2 marks.

14 Tom goes to a restaurant.
He can choose from three types of burgers and three types of side dishes.

Tom is going to choose one burger and one side dish.

List all the possible combinations Tom can choose.

Burger	Side
Beef	Salad
Veggie	Fries
Chicken	Potatoes

(2 marks)

Hint
- Use letters for the options. For example, use B for 'beef'.

Nearly there

BS, BF, BP, VS, VF, VP, CS, CF, CP, SB, SV, SC, FB, FV, FC, PB, PV, PC ....

....

The student has written too many combinations.

2 For each part of the question, write an improved answer that would be awarded full marks.

11 $A = 52000$ and $B = 3 \times 10^3$
Giving your answers in standard form, work out:

(a) $A + B$ **(2 marks)**

Hint
- To answer parts (a) and (b), work with ordinary numbers. Then, convert to standard form at the end.

Had a go

$5.2 \times 10^4 + 3 \times 10^3 = 8.2 \times 10^8$

8.2×10^8 ....

(b) AB **(2 marks)**

The student's final answer is not in standard form.

Nearly there

$5.2 \times 10^4 \times 3 \times 10^3 = 15.6 \times 10^7$

15.6×10^7 ....

3 Write an improved answer to each part of the question that would be awarded full marks.

4 Write the following numbers to the stated degree of accuracy.

(a) 0.07483 correct to three decimal places. **(1 mark)**

Had a go

0.0748 ....

(b) 0.07483 correct to three significant figures. **(1 mark)**

Had a go

0.075 ....

The student has confused the meanings of 'decimal places' and 'significant figures'.

Find the answer

1 For each part of the question, find the answer that would be awarded the mark. Choose **A**, **B** or **C**. Explain your choice.

6 (a) Write 0.00541 in standard form. **(1 mark)**

A 5.41×10^3 B 0.541×10^{-2} C 5.41×10^{-3}

Answer .... would get the mark because ....

....

....

(b) Write 4.2×10^5 as an ordinary number. **(1 mark)**

A 420000 B 4200000 C 0.000042

Answer .... would get the mark because ....

....

2 Use the hint below to find the answer that would be awarded 2 marks. Choose **A**, **B** or **C**. Explain your choice.

4 Ram buys a computer.
He pays £960 including VAT at 20%.

Work out the price of the computer without the VAT. **(2 marks)**

Hint

- Use the context of the question to check your answer makes sense — think about whether your answer should be more or less than the number given in the question.

A

20% of £960 = $\frac{20}{100} \times 960$
= £192
Price without VAT
= £960 − £192
= £768

B

Let 120% = £960
1% = $\frac{960}{120}$
100% = $\frac{960}{120} \times 100$
Price of computer = £800

C

Multiplier = 100% − 20%
= 80%
80% ÷ 100 = 0.8
Price of computer = £960 ÷ 0.8
= £1200

Answer .... would get 2 marks because ....

....

....

....

Mark the answer

1 Use the mark scheme to assign a mark to the answer.

Remember to find a common denominator before adding or subtracting fractions.

5 Work out $5\frac{3}{4}+\frac{7}{9}$

Give your answer as a mixed number in its simplest form. **(3 marks)**

$5\frac{3}{4}+\frac{7}{9} = 5+\frac{3}{4}+\frac{7}{9}$

$= 5+\frac{27}{36}+\frac{28}{36} = 5\frac{55}{36}$

$5\frac{55}{36}$ ....

Answer	Notes
$6\frac{19}{36}$	M1 for converting both fractions to get a common denominator of a multiple of 36, with at least one of the fractions correctly converted. M1 (dep on M1) for $5+\frac{"27"}{36}+\frac{"28"}{36}\left(=5\frac{55}{36}\right)$ A1 cao

I would award the answer .... out of 3 marks because ....

....

....

....

2 Use the mark scheme to assign a mark to the answer.

12 There are 75 students in a school. The school organises three trips. Each student can choose to go on one trip. They can go to a theme park, a castle or a zoo.

25 students choose the zoo.
40 students are girls.
15 girls choose the theme park.
17 boys choose the theme park.
Equal numbers of boys and girls choose the castle.

When I fill in a two-way table, I always check all the totals in the table match the totals in the question.

Complete the two-way table. **(3 marks)**

	Theme park	Castle	Zoo	Total
Girls	15	8	17	40
Boys	17	8	10	35
Total	32	18	25	75

Answer	Notes
15, 9, 16, 40 17, 9, 9, 35 32, 18, 25, 75	B1 for 15, 17, 25, 40, 75 B1 for 32 or 35 or 18 B1 for all correct entries

I would award the answer .... out of 3 marks because ....

....

....

....

Re-order the answer

1 Rearrange the working out into the most logical order by numbering each part. Use the hint to help.

6 Every evening, Diane cycles the same distance.

One evening, she stops for a rest when she has cycled exactly half the distance.

After a further 3 km, she has cycled exactly $\frac{5}{8}$ of the total distance.

How many kilometres does Diane cycle each evening? You must show your working. **(3 marks)**

Hint
- First, work out what fraction of the distance 3 km represents.

☐ $= 24$

☐ $\frac{1}{8}$ is equivalent to 3 km

☐ $\frac{5}{8} - \frac{1}{2}$

☐ 3×8

☐ $= \frac{5}{8} - \frac{4}{8} = \frac{1}{8}$

2 Rearrange the working out into the most logical order by numbering each part.

12 In January, Rob received £1500 commission on sales he had made that month.

In February, he received 20% less commission than he did in January.
In March, his commission was 15% higher than it was in February.
In April, his commission was 30% higher than it was in March.

How much commission did Rob receive in April? **(3 marks)**

☐ £1380 × 1.30

☐ £1500 × 0.8

☐ = £1794

☐ £1200 × 1.15

Complete the question

1 Use the student's answers to complete each part of the question.

Hint
- Write the missing power in the box.

5 (a) Write down the value of $9^{\square}$ **(1 mark)**

Nailed it!

........1........

(b) Write down the value of $9^{\square}$ **(1 mark)**

Nailed it!

........$\frac{1}{81}$........

(c) Write down the .... of $\frac{4}{9}$ **(1 mark)**

Nailed it!

........$\frac{9}{4}$........

2 Use the working out to complete the question.

3 Sandeep has 180 counters.
All of the counters are blue, yellow, green or red.

.... of the counters are blue.

$\frac{1}{3}$ of counters are yellow.

The ratio of the number of green counters to the number of red counters is .... : 2

Work out the .... of .... counters. **(5 marks)**

Nailed it!

This question tests your knowledge of ratio and proportion as well as your number skills.

25% of 180 = 0.25 × 180 = 45

$\frac{1}{3} \times 180 = 60$

45 + 60 = 105

180 − 105 = 75

$\frac{2}{5} \times 75 = 30$

........30........

3 Use the student's answer to complete the question.

Make sure you understand the key mathematical terms you have learnt.

4 A number, n, is rounded to .... decimal places.
The result is 6.17

Using ...., write down the .... for n. **(2 marks)**

Nailed it!

........$6.165 \leqslant n < 6.175$........

Complete the answer

1 For each part of the question, complete the student's answer so that it would be awarded full marks.

6 Gunnar orders some groceries. His shopping bill is shown.

3 cartons of juice at £1.45 each	£ 4.35
4 bottles of milk at 94p each	£ ....
1 loaf of bread	£1.25
5 bread rolls at 18p each	£ ....
2 blocks of cheese at £2.35 each	£ ....
Order total	£ ....
Delivery charge	£2.50
Total amount to pay	£ ....

Hints
- Read each line of the receipt carefully.
- Write all of your answers in pounds.

(a) Fill in the missing amounts. **(3 marks)**

(b) Gunnar pays with a £20 note.
How much change should he receive? **(2 marks)**

£20 – total amount = amount of change received

£ ....

2 Complete the student's answer so that it would be awarded 4 marks.

15 A car costs £9950 before a sale. In the sale, the price is reduced by 12%.

Helga buys the car during the sale.
She puts down a deposit of £3422
She will pay off the rest of the cost in 24 equal payments.

How much is each payment?
You must show all your working. **(4 marks)**

Read the question carefully and underline key words.

100% – 12% = 88%

£ ....

Improve the answer

1 Write an improved answer that would be awarded 2 marks.

7 Work out an estimate for the value of $\frac{4.93 \times 306}{0.5023}$ **(2 marks)**

Nearly there

$\frac{5 \times 300}{1} = \frac{1500}{1} = 1500$

........1500........ ....

When estimating, I usually round each number to 1 significant figure.

2 Write an improved answer that would be awarded 4 marks.

16 Andrea works in a shop.
Her normal rate of pay is £8 per hour.

When Andrea works more than 7 hours a day, she is paid an overtime rate for each hour she works after the first 7 hours.

Andrea's rate of overtime pay per hour is $1\frac{1}{4}$ times her normal rate of pay per hour.

On Saturday Andrea worked for 11 hours.
She thinks that she should have earned more than £100 on this Saturday.

Is she correct?
You must show your working. **(4 marks)**

Had a go

$\frac{1}{4}$ of £8 = £2

Overtime rate = £8 + £2 = £10

Total pay = 11 × £10

= £110

Yes, she has earned more than £100

The student has incorrectly applied the overtime rate to all the hours worked.

....

Find the answer

1 For each part of the question, find the answer that would be awarded the mark. Choose **A**, **B** or **C**. Explain your choice.

3 (a) Write the number forty thousand and sixty-three in digits. **(1 mark)**

A 40630 B 40063 C 4063

Answer .... would get the mark because ....

....

(b) Write down the value of the 5 in the number 745 638 **(1 mark)**

A 5000 B 50 000 C 500

Answer .... would get the mark because ....

....

2 Find the answer that would be awarded the mark. Choose **A**, **B** or **C**. Explain your choice.

5 Work out the value of 2^5 **(1 mark)**

A $2 + 2 + 2 + 2 + 2 = 10$ B $2 \times 5 = 10$ C $2 \times 2 \times 2 \times 2 \times 2 = 32$

Answer .... would get the mark because ....

....

....

3 Find the answer that would be awarded the mark. Choose **A**, **B** or **C**. Explain your choice.

1 Write $\frac{4}{5}$ as a percentage. **(1 mark)**

A $\frac{4}{5} \times 100 = 0.8 \times 100 = 80\%$

B $\frac{4}{5} \times 100 = 0.8 \times 100 = 8\%$

C $\frac{4}{5} = 0.8$

Answer .... would get the mark because ....

....

....

Re-order the answer

1 Rearrange the working out into the most logical order by numbering each part. Use the hint to help.

3 Work out $3\frac{4}{5} - 1\frac{2}{3}$

Give your answer as a mixed number. **(3 marks)**

Hints
- Work out the answer for yourself.
- Compare this working with your own.

☐ $= 2\frac{2}{15}$

☐ $= \frac{19}{5} - \frac{5}{3}$

☐ $= \frac{32}{15}$

☐ $= \frac{57}{15} - \frac{25}{15}$

2 Rearrange the working out into the most logical order by numbering each part.

13 The price of a television is reduced by 15% in a sale.

The sale price of the television is £765

Work out the price of the television before the sale. **(3 marks)**

This question tests your knowledge of proportion as well as your number skills.

☐ 100% = £9 × 100

☐ 100% − 15% = 85%

☐ 100% = £900

☐ 85% = £765

☐ 1% = £765 ÷ 85 = £9

Complete the question

1 Use the student's answers to complete each part of the question.

3 Here is a list of numbers

2 7 12 16 22 27

From the numbers in the list, write down:

Hint
- Think about what **types** of numbers the answers are.

(a) the .... number **(1 mark)**

Nailed it!

..........16..........

(b) the .... number **(1 mark)**

Nailed it!

..........27..........

(c) the .... numbers. **(1 mark)**

Nailed it!

.......2 and 7.......

2 Use the student's working out and answer to complete the question.

16 .... spheres have a total weight of .... grams.

.... spheres and .... cubes have a total weight of .... grams.

Work out the total weight, in grams, of .... spheres and .... cubes. **(4 marks)**

Nailed it!

Hints
- If you find this difficult, make up some numbers to fill the gaps, and work out the answer.
- Then, compare the working with your own.
- Adjust the numbers in the question to match.

1400g ÷ 4 = 350g

5 × 350g = 1750g

2200g − 1750g = 450g

450g ÷ 3 = 150g

(3 × 350g) + (2 × 150g) = 1050g + 300g = 1350g

.....1350..... g

3 Use the student's working out and answer to complete the question.

Hint
- The 'Side' column should remain empty in the question.

12 Michael is the manager of a swimming club.

He interviews some swimmers to find out their favourite swimming stroke.
The table shows this information.

Stroke	....	Butterfly	Crawl	Side
Proportion	....	....	....	

Write the swimming strokes in .... of popularity.

Start with the .... popular. **(3 marks)**

$\frac{6}{25} = 0.24$, $\frac{1}{4} = 0.25$,

0.24 + 0.25 + 0.28 = 0.77

1 − 0.77 = 0.23

0.23, $\frac{6}{25}$, $\frac{1}{4}$, 0.28

side, back, crawl, butterfly

Improve the answer

1 Write an improved answer that would be awarded 2 marks.

10 Work out 3 × (4 + 6 ÷ 2) **(2 marks)**

The student has not applied BIDMAS within the brackets.

Nearly there

3 × (10 ÷ 2) = 3 × 5 = 15

..........15..........

....

2 Write an improved answer that would be awarded 4 marks.

16 Calvino buys 80 mangoes for £60

He sells 12 boxes of six mangoes at £6.50 per box.
The rest of the mangoes are sold at 95p each.

Work out how much profit he makes. **(4 marks)**

The student has not converted 95p to pounds.

Nearly there

12 × 6.50 = 78

12 × 6 = 72

80 − 72 = 8

8 × 95 = 760

78 + 760 = 838

Profit = £838 − £60 = £778

£..........778..........

£........................

3 Write an improved answer that would be awarded 3 marks.

11 In a shop, pencil cases cost £1.75 each.

Taran has £20
He wants to buy as many pencil cases as possible.

How many can he buy and how much change should he receive? **(3 marks)**

Had a go

20 ÷ 1.75 = 11.428

Cost of pencil cases = 12 × 1.75 = £21

Change = £21 − £20 = £1

Taran can buy 12 pencil cases. He should receive £1 change.

If I have time, I read through the question again and make sure my working and answer make sense. This helps me spot silly mistakes!

....

Find the answer

1 Find the answer that would be awarded 2 marks. Choose **A**, **B** or **C**. Explain your choice.

4 Work out 60% of 120 **(2 marks)**

A
10% = 120 ÷ 10 = 12
60% = 6 × 12
= 72

B
10% = 120 ÷ 100 = 1.2
60% = 6 × 1.2
= 7.2

C
10% = 120 ÷ 10 = 12
40% = 4 × 12
60% = 100 − 48 = 52

Answer .... would get 2 marks because ....

....

2 For each part of the question, find the answer that would be awarded the mark. Choose **A**, **B** or **C**. Explain your choice.

5 Write these calculations as a single power.

(a) $5^4 \times 5^2$ **(1 mark)**

A $5^{4-2} = 5^2$

B $5^{4+2} = 5^6$

C $25^{4+2} = 25^8$

Answer .... would get the mark because ....

....

(b) $5^9 \div 5^6$ **(1 mark)**

A $5^{9-6} = 5^3$

B $5^{9+6} = 5^{15}$

C $1^{9-6} = 1^3$

Answer .... would get the mark because ....

....

(c) $(5^4)^3$ **(1 mark)**

A $5^{4-3} = 5^1$

B $5^{4+3} = 5^7$

C $5^{4\times3} = 5^{12}$

Answer .... would get the mark because ....

....

3 Find the answer that would be awarded the mark. Choose **A**, **B** or **C**. Explain your choice.

3 Work out $\sqrt{64} \times \sqrt[3]{27}$ **(1 mark)**

A $8 \times 3 = 24$

B $4 \times 3 = 12$

C $8 \times 9 = 72$

Answer .... would get the mark because ....

....

Mark the answer

1 Use the mark scheme to assign a mark to the answer. Explain your decision.

18 Ruth is going to have a party. There will be 60 people at the party.
Ruth wants to buy enough samosas so that each person at the party can have 2 samosas.
There are 7 samosas in each pack. Ruth buys 16 packs of samosas.

Has she bought enough samosas? **(3 marks)**

Number of samosas needed = 60 × 2 = 120

Number of samosas Ruth buys = 16 × 7 = 112

..........112..........

Answer	Notes
No as 112 < 120	P1 process to find the number of samosas needed e.g. 60 × 2 (=120) P1 process to find the number of samosas bought e.g. 16 × 7 (= 112) A1 cao

I would award the answer .... out of 3 marks because ....

....

....

....

2 Use the mark scheme to assign marks to the answers. Explain your decisions.

4 (a) Find the highest common factor (HCF) of 32 and 48 **(2 marks)**

32 = 1 × 32, 2 × 16, 4 × 8

48 = 1 × 48, 2 × 24, 3 × 16, 4 × 12, 6 × 8

Factors of 32: 1, 2, 4, 8, 16, 32

Factors of 48: 1, 2, 3, 4, 6, 8, 12, 16, 24, 48

HCF = 16

I make sure I write down all my working because I know I might not get all the marks if I don't – even if my final answer is correct.

..........16..........

Answer	Notes
16	M1 lists the factors of 32 and 48 A1 cao

I would award the answer .... out of 2 marks because ....

....

(b) Find the lowest common multiple (LCM) of 32 and 48 **(2 marks)**

Multiples of 32: 32, 64, 96, 128, 160

Multiples of 48: 48, 96 LCM = 96

..........96..........

Answer	Notes
96	M1 lists the multiples of 32 and 48 A1 cao

I would award the answer .... out of 2 marks because ....

....

Complete the question

1 Use the student's working out and answer to complete the question.

17 The alarms on Sandra's and Pavel's phones sound together at .... am.

Sandra's alarm then sounds every .... minutes.

Pavel's alarm then sounds every .... minutes.

Show that both of their alarms will next sound together at .... am. **(3 marks)**

Nailed it!

Sandra:	8	16	24	32	40	48	56	64	72	80	88	96
Pavel:	11	22	33	44	55	66	77	88	99			

88 minutes = 1 hour 28 minutes

7.30 + 1 h 28 = 8.58

2 Use the student's working out and answer to complete the question.

Hint
- The question uses mixed units of length.

11 Adam has .... m of rope on a reel.
He cuts 4 pieces of rope off the reel.

The lengths of the pieces are .... cm, ... m, ... m and .... cm.

Work out how much rope, in .... , Adam has .... on the reel. **(3 marks)**

Nailed it!

95 + 443 + 1065 + 167 = 1770

2000 − 1770 = 230

Amount of rope on the reel = 2.3 m

2.3 m

3 Use the student's working out and answer to complete the question.

20 The diagram shows a large circle and .... small circles.

Area of circle B = $\frac{3}{2}\pi$ cm^2

The area of circle B is .... the area of circle A.

The area of the .... circle is .... times the area of circle B.

Work out the .... area. Leave your .... in terms of ....

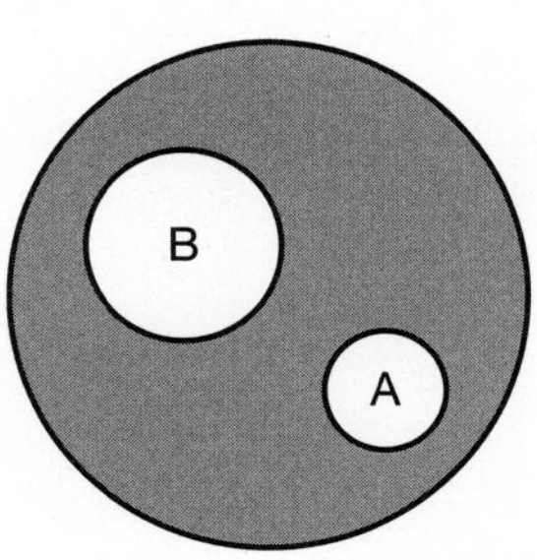

(3 marks)

Nailed it!

Area of circle A = $\frac{3}{4}\pi$ cm^2

Area of large circle = $\frac{18}{2}\pi = 9\pi$ cm^2

Shaded area = $9\pi - \frac{3}{2}\pi - \frac{3}{4}\pi = \frac{36}{4}\pi - \frac{6}{4}\pi - \frac{3}{4}\pi = \frac{27}{4}\pi$

$\frac{27}{4}\pi$ cm^2

Complete the answer

1 Use the hint below to complete the student's answer so that it would be awarded 3 marks.

9 Washing powder is sold in three sizes: 2 kg, 5 kg and 9 kg.

A 2 kg box of washing powder costs £1.79
A 5 kg box of washing powder costs £4.40
A 9 kg box of washing powder costs £8.10

Which size is the best value for money?
You must show how you get your answer.

(3 marks)

Hint

- Work out the cost per kilogram for each size of box.

2 kg box = 1.79 ÷ 2 = £0.895

....

2 Use the hint below to complete the student's answer so that it would be awarded 3 marks.

6 Leon and Sal both work in restaurants.

Leon gets basic pay of £80 per day.
Sal gets basic pay of £84 per day.

One day, Leon gets a bonus of 30% of his basic pay.
On the same day, Sal gets £15 in tips.

Hint

- First, work out the total amounts of money that Leon and Sal each get that day.

Work out the difference between the total amounts of money that Leon and Sal each get that day. **(3 marks)**

10% of £80 = £8

30% of £80 =

£ ....

3 Use the hints below to complete the student's answer so that it would be awarded 3 marks.

3 Express 180 as a product of its prime factors. **(3 marks)**

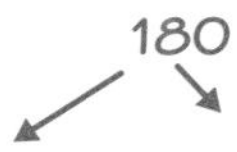

Hints

- Use the factor tree to help you divide 180 until you reach its prime factors.
- Remember to use indices in your answer.
- It doesn't matter what your factor tree looks like, as long as you have the correct final answer.

....

Improve the answer

1 For each part of the question, write an improved answer that would be awarded full marks.

20 Here is a grid showing the points *A* and *B*.

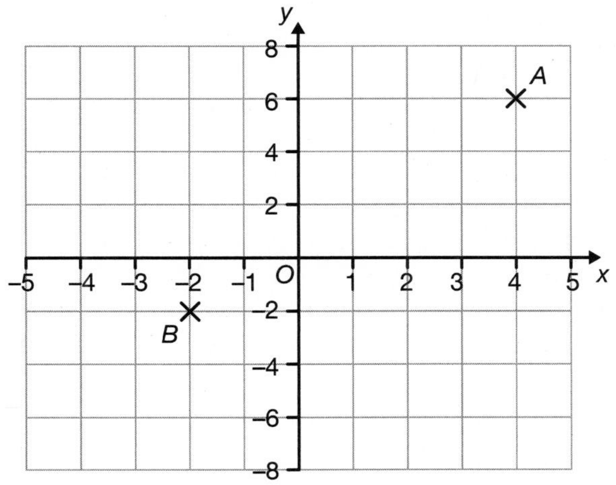

(a) Write down the coordinates of the points *A* and *B*. **(2 marks)**

Had a go

A (6, 4) .... *A* ....

B (−2, 2) .... *B* ....

(b) Write down the coordinates of the midpoint of *AB*. **(2 marks)**

Had a go

(2, 1) ....

Hint

- Draw the line *AB* on the grid and count the squares to find the midpoint.

2 Write an improved answer that would be awarded 2 marks.

8 Work out the value of *v*.

$v = u + at$ $u = 2$ $a = -5$ $t = \frac{1}{3}$ **(2 marks)**

Nearly there

$v = 2 + (-5)\left(\frac{1}{3}\right)$

$v = 2 + \frac{5}{3}$

$v = \frac{6}{3} + \frac{5}{3}$

$v = \frac{11}{3}$

$\frac{11}{3}$ ....

The student has correctly substituted the values into the equation but has made a mistake in their attempt to solve it.

Find the answer

1 For each part of the question, find the answer that would be awarded full marks. Choose **A**, **B** or **C**. Explain your choice.

(a) Simplify $5x + 4y + 3x - 9y$ **(2 marks)**

A $8x - 5y$ B $2x - 13y$ C $8x + 5y$

Answer .... would get 2 marks because ....

....

(b) Factorise $y^2 - 4y$ **(1 mark)**

A $y(y + 4)$ B $y(y - 4)$ C $4y(y - 1)$

Answer .... would get the mark because ....

....

(c) Expand $y(y^3 + 2y)$ **(2 marks)**

A $y^4 + 2y$ B $y^3 + 2y^2$ C $y^4 + 2y^2$

Answer .... would get 2 marks because ....

....

2 Find the answer that would be awarded 3 marks. Choose **A**, **B** or **C**. Explain your choice.

4 Here are three graphs.

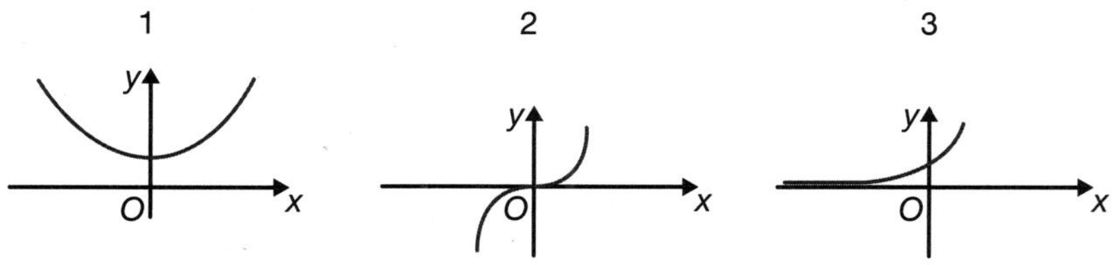

Here are four equations of graphs.

$y = 3^x$ $y = x^3$ $y = x^2 + 3$ $y = \frac{2}{x}$

Match each graph to the correct equation. **(3 marks)**

A
1 is $y = x^2 + 3$
2 is $y = x^3$
3 is $y = 3^x$

B
1 is $y = x^3$
2 is $y = x^2 + 3$
3 is $y = 3^x$

C
1 is $y = x^3$
2 is $y = x^2 + 3$
3 is $y = \frac{2}{x}$

Answer .... would get 3 marks because ....

....

Mark the answer

1 Use the mark scheme to assign a mark to the answer. Explain your decision.

13 Solve the simultaneous equations

① $3x + 10y = 7$
② $x - 4y = 6$

(3 marks)

③: ② × 3 $3x - 12y = 18$

③ − ① $22y = -11$

$y = -0.5$

Substitute $3x + 10(-0.5) = 7$

$3x = 7 - 5$

$x = \frac{2}{3}$

$x = \frac{2}{3}, y = -\frac{1}{2}$

Answer	Notes
$x = 4, y = -0.5$	M1 for a correct method to eliminate one variable M1 for a correct method to find second variable A1 for $x = 4, y = -0.5$

I would award the answer .... out of 3 marks because ....

....

....

....

2 Use the mark scheme to assign a mark to the answer. Explain your decision.

14 Albert has x counters. Ben has twice as many counters as Albert. Chris has 7 more counters than Albert. They have a total of 43 counters.

Work out how many counters Albert, Ben and Chris each have. **(5 marks)**

$x + 2x + x + 7 = 4x + 7 = 43$

$4x = 36$

$x = 9$

$2x = 2 \times 9 = 18$

$x + 7 = 9 + 7 = 16$

Albert has 9 counters, Ben has 18 and Chris has 16

Answer	Notes
9, 18 and 16	P1 process to set up an expression for the total number of counters e.g. $x + 2x + x + 7$ or $4x + 7$ P1 process to set up an equation for the counters e.g. $x + 2x + x + 7 = 43$ or $4x + 7 = 43$ P1 process to solve the equation e.g. $x = (43 - 7) \div 4$ (= 9) P1 process to work out the numbers of counters e.g. 2 × 9 and 9 + 7 A1 for 9, 18 and 16

I would award the answer .... out of 5 marks because ....

....

Re-order the answer

1 Rearrange the working out into the most logical order by numbering each part. Use the hints to help.

11 Solve $\frac{7^6 \times 7^x}{7^2} = 7^5$ **(4 marks)**

☐ $6 + x - 2 = 5$

☐ $\frac{7^{6+x}}{7^2} = 7^5$

☐ $x = 1$

☐ $7^{6+x-2} = 7^5$

☐ $x = 5 + 2 - 6$

Hints

- Deal with the powers in the numerator first.
- Then, look at the denominator.

2 Rearrange the working out into the most logical order by numbering each part. Use the hint to help.

20 The diagram shows a triangle.

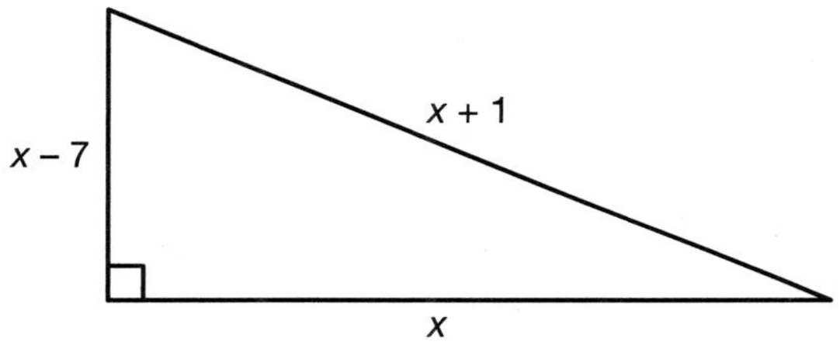

In the diagram, all the measurements are in centimetres.

The perimeter of the triangle is 30 cm.
The area of the triangle is A cm².

Work out the value of A. **(4 marks)**

Hint

- First, set up an equation and solve it to find the value of x.

☐ $x = 12$

☐ $= 30$

☐ $3x = 36$

☐ $x + x - 7 + x + 1 = 30$

☐ $0.5 \times 12 \times 5$

Complete the question

1 Use the student's working out and answer to complete the question.

7 Expand and simplify (..............)(..............) **(2 marks)**

Nailed it!

$x^2 + 6x - 4x - 24 = x^2 + 2x - 24$

$x^2 + 2x - 24$

Hint

- You need to provide an expression as two brackets. It doesn't matter which way round you write them into the question; the answer will still be the same.

2 Use the student's answer to complete the question.

10 Write down the .... represented on the number line. **(1 mark)**

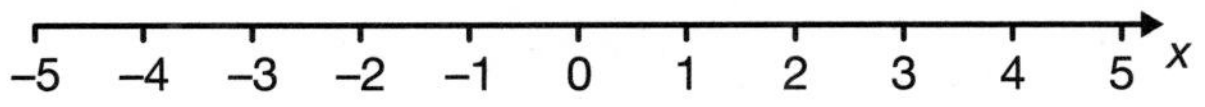

Nailed it!

$-2 < x \leq 3$

3 Use the student's working out and answer to complete each part of the question.

17 (a) **A** and **B** are straight lines.

Line **A** has equation ....$y =$.........$x +$.........

Line **B** goes through the points (.........,.........) and (.........,.........).

Do lines **A** and **B** ....?

You must explain your answer. **(3 marks)**

Nailed it!

$y = \frac{4}{2}x + \frac{7}{2} \rightarrow y = 2x + \frac{7}{2}$

$\text{Gradient} = \frac{8-2}{1+1} = \frac{6}{2} = 3$

Yes, because they are not parallel (the gradients are not equal).

Hint

- What do you know about parallel lines?

(b) The line **C** is .... to the line **A**.

The line **C** passes through the point (.........,.........).

Find an .... of line **C**. **(2 marks)**

Nailed it!

$y = 2x + c$

$4 = 2(-3) + c$

$4 = -6 + c$

$c = 4 + 6$

$c = 10$

$y = 2x + 10$

Complete the answer

1 For each part of the question, complete the student's answer so that it would be awarded full marks.

9 (a) Complete the table of values for $y = 3x + 4$ **(2 marks)**

x	−2	−1	0	1	2	3
y	−2		4			13

$y = 3x + 4 = 3(-2) + 4 = -6 + 4 = -2$

Hint

- Use the same method to work out the remaining missing values.

(b) On the grid, draw the graph of $y = 3x + 4$ **(2 marks)**

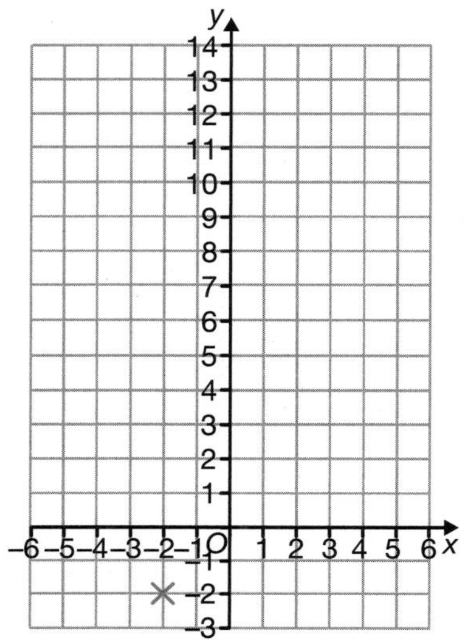

When I'm drawing a straight-line graph, I know I've made a mistake if the points don't all lie on the line.

2 For each part of the question, complete the student's answer so that it would be awarded full marks.

4 Here are the first four terms of an arithmetic sequence.

4 9 14 19

(a) Write down the next two terms of the sequence. **(1 mark)**

4 → 9 → 14 → 19

+5 +5 +5

Hint

- Use the term-to-term rule to generate the next two terms.

....

(b) Write an expression, in terms of n, for the nth term of the sequence. **(2 marks)**

$5n$

Hint

- $5n$ is part of the expression for the nth term. Use the term-to-term rule to find term 0 and complete the expression.

....

Improve the answer

1 Write an improved answer that would be awarded 3 marks.

4 Solve $x^2 - 5x - 24 = 0$ **(3 marks)**

Nearly there

$(+8) \times (-3) = -24$ and $(+8) + (-3) = 5$

$(x + 8)(x - 3) = 0$

$(x + 8) = 0$ or $(x - 3) = 0$

$x = -8$ or $x = 3$

$x = -8$ or $x = 3$

The student has attempted to factorise but has made an error with the signs.

....

2 Write an improved answer that would be awarded 4 marks.

8 ABC is a triangle.

Angle *ABC* = angle ACB
Length of side *AB* = $(3x + 8)$ cm
Length of side *AC* = $(20 - x)$ cm
Length of side *BC* = $(3x)$ cm

Work out the perimeter, in cm, of the triangle.

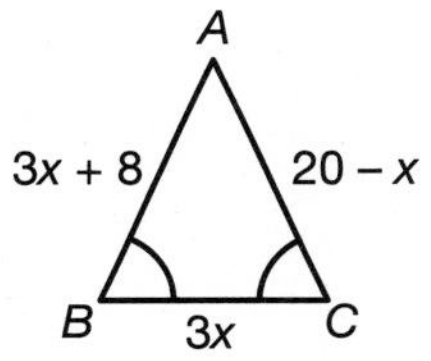

(4 marks)

Nearly there

$3x + 8 = 20 - x$

$3x + x = 20 + 8$

$4x = 28$

$x = 7$

Perimeter $= 3(7) + 8 + 20 - 7 + 3(7)$

$= 21 + 8 + 20 - 7 + 21$

$= 63$

63 cm

The student has correctly identified that the triangle is isosceles and set up an equation. However, they have made an error when attempting to solve it.

.... cm

Find the answer

1 For each part of the question, find the answer that would be awarded full marks. Choose **A**, **B** or **C**. Explain your choice.

7 (a) Simplify $3(2x - 1) - 2(2x - 3)$ **(2 marks)**

A: $6x - 3 - 4x + 6 = 2x + 3$

B: $6x - 3 - 4x - 6 = 2x - 9$

C: $6x - 3 - 4x + 6 = 2x - 3$

Answer .... would get 2 marks because ....

....

....

(b) Simplify $4x^4y^5 \times 3x^2y^3$ **(2 marks)**

A: $12 \times x^8 \times y^{15} = 12x^8y^{15}$

B: $12 \times x^6 \times y^8 = 12x^6y^8$

C: $7 \times x^6 \times y^8 = 7x^6y^8$

Answer .... would get 2 marks because ....

....

2 Find the answer that would be awarded 4 marks. Choose **A**, **B** or **C**. Explain your choice.

20 By drawing two suitable straight lines on a coordinate grid, solve the simultaneous equations.

$$y = x + 1$$
$$x + y = 7$$

(4 marks)

A

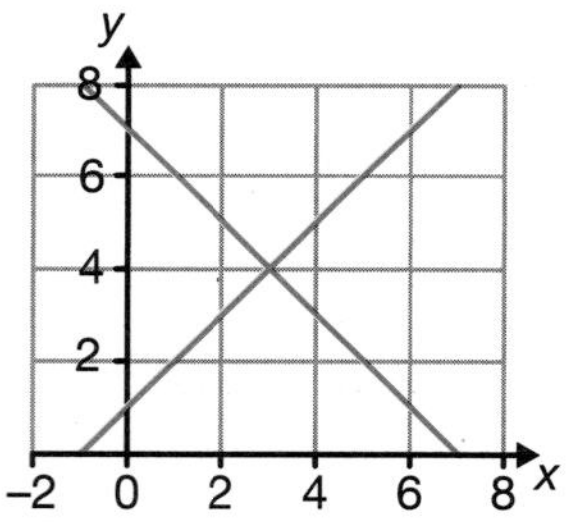

$x = 3,\ y = 4$

B

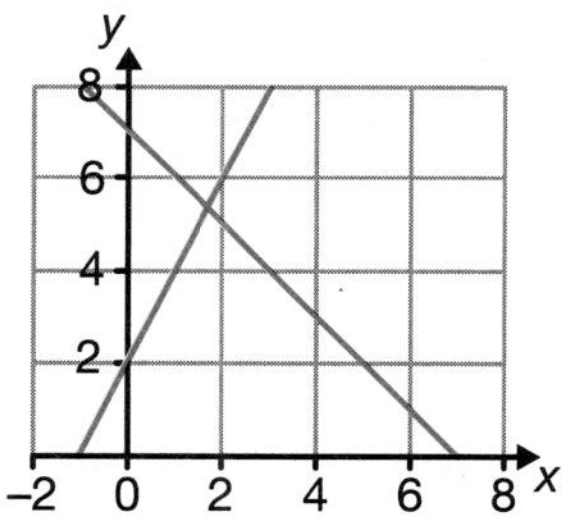

$x = 1.5,\ y = 5$

C

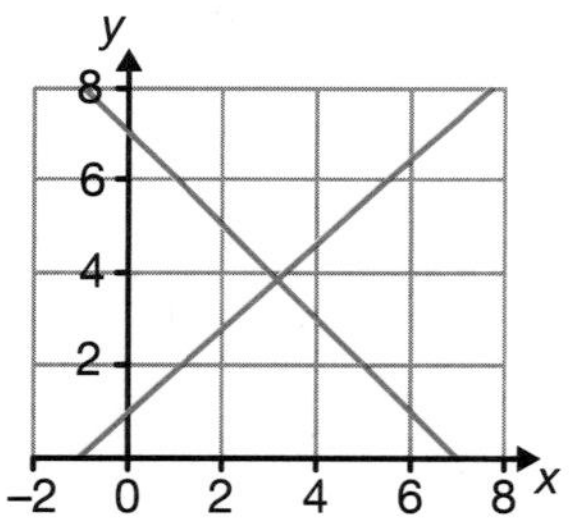

$x = 4,\ y = 3$

Answer .... would get 4 marks because ....

....

Mark the answer

1 Use the mark scheme to assign a mark to the answer. Explain your decision.

3 The nth term of a sequence is $2n^2 - 15$

Work out the 4th term of this sequence. **(1 mark)**

$2 \times 4^2 - 15 = 8^2 - 15 = 64 - 15 = 49$

........49........

Answer	Notes
17	B1 cao

I would award the answer .... out of 1 mark because ....

....

2 Use the mark scheme to assign a mark to the answer. Explain your decision.

8 The diagram shows a patio in the shape of a trapezium.

All the measurements are in metres.
The area of the patio is 220 m².

Work out the value of x. **(5 marks)**

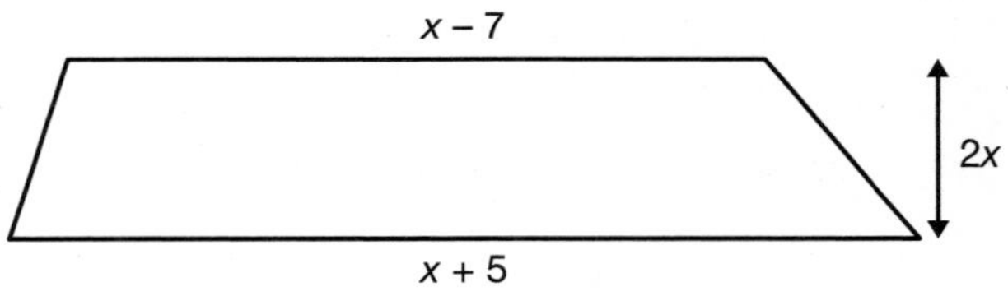

$220 = \frac{1}{2}(x - 7 + x + 5)(2x)$

$= \frac{1}{2}(2x - 2)(2x)$

$= (x)(2x - 2)$

$= 2x^2 - 2x$

So $2x^2 - 2x - 220 = 0$

$x^2 - x - 110 = 0$

$(x - 10)(x + 11) = 0$

$x = 10$ or $x = -11$

........$x = 10$........

Answer	Notes
11	P1 process to use the trapezium rule with correct lengths e.g. $\frac{1}{2}(x - 7 + x + 5)(2x)$ P1 process to set up an equation e.g. $\frac{1}{2}(x - 7 + x + 5)(2x) = 220$ P1 process to write the equation in the form $ax^2 + bx + c = 0$ e.g. $2x^2 - 2x - 220 = 0$ P1 process to solve the quadratic equation e.g. $(x - 11)(x + 10) = 0$ A1 $x = 11$

I would award the answer .... out of 5 marks because ....

....

....

....

Find the answer

1 For each part of the question, find the answer that would be awarded full marks. Choose **A, B** or **C**. Explain your choice.

15 (a) Show that $(x - 2)^2 \equiv x^2 - 4x + 4$ **(2 marks)**

A	B	C
$(x-2)^2 = (x-2)(x-2)$ $= x^2 - 2x - 2x + 4$ $= x^2 - 4x + 4$	$(x-2)^2 = (x-2)(x+2)$ $= x^2 - 2x + 2x - 4$ $= x^2 - 4x + 4$	$(x-2)^2 = (x-2)(x-2)$ $= x^2 + 2x + 2x + 4$ $= x^2 - 4x + 4$

Answer .... would get 2 marks because ....

....

(b) Using your answer from part (a), show that $(x + 2)^2 + (x - 2)^2 \equiv 2(x^2 + 4)$. **(2 marks)**

A	B	C
$(x+2)^2 = (x+2)(x+2)$ $= x^2 + 2x + 2x + 4$ $= x^2 + 4x + 4$ $x^2 + 4x + 4 + x^2 - 4x + 4$ $= 2x^2 + 8$	$(x+2)^2 = (x+2)(x+2)$ $= x^2 + 2x + 2x + 4$ $= x^2 + 4x + 4$ $x^2 + 4x + 4 + x^2 - 4x + 4$ $= 2x^2 + 8$ $= 2(x^2 + 4)$	$(x+2)^2 = (x+2)(x+2)$ $= x^2 + 2x + 2x + 4$ $= x^2 + 4x + 4$ $x^2 + 4x + 4 + x^2 - 4x + 4$ $= 2x^2 + 8x$ $= 2(x^2 + 4x)$

Answer .... would get 2 marks because ....

....

....

....

2 Find the answer that would be awarded the mark. Choose **A, B** or **C**. Explain your choice.

8 x is greater than −4 and less than 7
Write the information as a single inequality. **(1 mark)**

A $x > -4$ and $x < 7$ B $-4 > x > 7$ C $-4 < x < 7$

Answer .... would get the mark because ....

....

3 Find the answer that would be awarded the mark. Choose **A, B** or **C**. Explain your choice.

10 Rearrange $x = y + 7$ to make y the subject. **(1 mark)**

A $y = x + 7$ B $y = x - 7$ C $x + y = 7$

Answer .... would get the mark because ....

....

Complete the answer

1 Use the hint below to complete the student's answer so that it would be awarded 3 marks.

4 List the integer values that satisfy the inequality $-1 < 2x - 1 \leqslant 10$ **(3 marks)**

$-1 < 2x - 1$ $\quad\quad$ $2x - 1 \leqslant 10$

Hint
- Treat $-1 < 2x - 1 \leqslant 10$ as two separate inequalities. Solve them both for x.

....

2 Use the hints below to complete the student's answer so that it would be awarded 2 marks.

11 The table shows the values for a straight line.

x	–1	0	1	2	3
y	–8	–5	–2	1	4

Work out the equation of the line. **(2 marks)**

Gradient goes up 3 and across 1

Hints
- The gradient, m, is $\frac{\text{change in } y}{\text{change in } x}$.
- The y-intercept, c, is the y-value when $x = 0$
- Write your answer in the form $y = mx + c$.

....

3 Use the hint below to complete the student's answer so that it would be awarded 3 marks.

11 $\frac{x}{3} = 4$ and $\frac{20}{y} = 4$

Work out xy. **(3 marks)**

$x = 4 \times 3$

$= 12$

Hint
- First, work out the values of x and y.

....

4 Use the hint below to complete the student's answer so that it would be awarded 3 marks.

17 $P = 3n + m$.
n is an integer and m is one more than n.
Show that P is always an odd number. **(3 marks)**

$m = n + 1$

Hint
- Write P in terms of n only.

....

Improve the answer

1 Write an improved answer that would be awarded 2 marks.

13 Factorise fully $6x^4y + 24x^3y^4$ **(2 marks)**

Nearly there

$6x^3y(x + 3y^3)$ ....

The student has made a mistake with one of the factors.

2 Write an improved answer that would be awarded 3 marks.

8 $3x + 4 + ax + b = 2(5x + 3)$

Given that a and b are integers, work out the value of a and the value of b. **(3 marks)**

Nearly there

$ax + b = 2(5x + 3) - 3x + 4$

$= 10x + 6 - 3x + 4$

$= 7x + 10$

$a =$ 7 $a =$ ....

$b =$ 10 $b =$ ....

The student has identified the need to subtract $3x + 4$ from $2(5x + 3)$ but has made a mistake in their working.

3 Write an improved answer that would be awarded 3 marks.

7 Solve $\frac{12-2x}{4} = 6$ **(3 marks)**

Nearly there

$12 - 2x = 24$

$-2x = 24 + 12$

$-2x = 36$

$x = \frac{36}{-2}$

$x = -18$

-18 ....

The student has correctly multiplied out the denominator, but has then made a mistake in their working.

Find the answer

1 Find the answer that would be awarded the mark. Choose **A**, **B** or **C**. Explain your choice.

4 Simplify $x^6 \div x^2$ **(1 mark)**

A $x^{6+2} = x^8$

B $x^{6 \div 2} = x^3$

C $x^{6-2} = x^4$

Answer .... would get the mark because ....

....

2 Find the answer that would be awarded 2 marks. Choose **A**, **B** or **C**. Explain your choice.

10 Factorise $3x^2 - 48$ **(2 marks)**

A $3(x^2 - 16) = 3(x - 4)(x - 4)$

B $3(x^2 - 16)$

C $3(x^2 - 16) = 3(x - 4)(x + 4)$

Answer .... would get 2 marks because ....

....

3 Find the answer that would be awarded 2 marks. Choose **A**, **B** or **C**. Explain your choice.

5 Solve $6x + 4 \geqslant x + 24$ **(2 marks)**

A
$6x + x \geqslant 24 + 4$
$7x \geqslant 28$
$x \geqslant 4$

B
$6x - x \geqslant 24 - 4$
$5x \geqslant 20$
$x \geqslant 4$

C
$6x - x \geqslant 24 - 4$
$4x \geqslant 14$
$x \geqslant 3.5$

Answer .... would get 2 marks because ....

....

4 Find the answer that would be awarded 2 marks. Choose **A**, **B** or **C**. Explain your choice.

7 A shop sells boxes of pencils in two sizes, small and large.

There are 5 pencils in each small box.
There are 7 pencils in each large box.

Xian buys x small boxes of pencils and y large boxes of pencils.

Write down an expression, in terms of x and y, for the total number of pencils Xian buys. **(2 marks)**

A $5x + 7y$

B $7x + 5y$

C $35xy$

Answer .... would get 2 marks because ....

....

Complete the answer

1 Complete parts (b), (c) and (d) of the student's answer so that they would be awarded full marks.

15 (a) Complete the table of values for $y = x^2 - 5x + 3$ **(2 marks)**

Nailed it!

x	−1	0	1	2	3	4	5
y	9	3	−1	−3	−3	−1	3

(b) On the grid, draw the graph of $y = x^2 - 5x + 3$ for all values of x from −1 to 5 **(2 marks)**

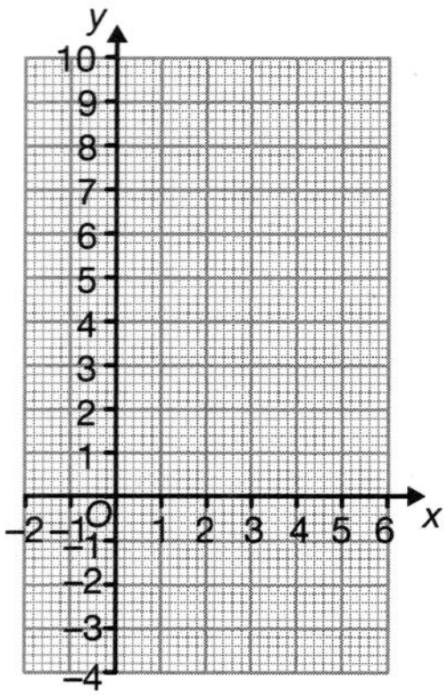

Hint

- Read off the x values where the graph crosses the x-axis.

(c) Estimate the solutions to the equation $x^2 - 5x + 3 = 0$ **(2 marks)**

....

(d) Write down the coordinates of the turning point of the equation $x^2 - 5x + 3 = 0$ **(1 mark)**

Hint

- The turning point is the maximum or minimum point on the curve.

....

2 Use the hint below to complete the student's answer so that it would be awarded 3 marks.

14 A, B and C are expressions, where $B = 29$

$A = 6x - 7$ $\quad B = 4x + 5$ $\quad C = 5x - 1$

Does $A = C$?
You must show your working. **(3 marks)**

Hint

- Use $B = 29$ to find the value of x.

$4x + 5 = 29$

....

Improve the answer

1 Write an improved answer that would be awarded 2 marks.

> The student has not given their answer in its simplest form.

12 Connor has 16 red beads and 24 blue beads.

Write the ratio of the number of red beads to the number of blue beads.
Give your answer in its simplest form. **(2 marks)**

Nearly there

Number of red beads : number of blue beads

16 : 24

........16 : 24........ ....

2 Write an improved answer that would be awarded 2 marks.

> The student's working is correct, but they have not read the question properly.

14 A school rugby team plays 55 games of rugby.

The ratio of the number of games they win to the number of games they do **not** win is 7 : 4

Work out the number of games the team does not win. **(2 marks)**

Nearly there

Total number of parts = 7 + 4 = 11

11 parts = 55 games so 1 part = 55 ÷ 11 = 5

Number of games won = 7 × 5 = 35

........35........ ....

3 Write an improved answer that would be awarded 2 marks.

> The student has correctly found the interest for the first year, but has misunderstood the concept of compound interest.

14 Mei invests £8000 in a savings bond for n years.
She receives 3% compound interest each year.

At the end of n years Mei has £8741.82 in her savings bond.

Work out the value of n.
You must show your working. **(2 marks)**

Had a go

£8000 × 0.03 = £240

£8000 + £240 + £240 + £240 = £8720

£8720 + £240 = £8960

........$n = 4$........ ....

Complete the answer

1 Use the hints below to complete the student's answer so that it would be awarded 5 marks.

8 An aeroplane is carrying some passengers.
Each passenger has a standard ticket or a discounted ticket.

The ratio of the number of adult passengers to the number of child passengers is 4 : 3

$\frac{3}{4}$ of the child passengers have discounted tickets.

15 child passengers have standard tickets.
The maximum number of tickets available for this aeroplane is 200

Show that 70% of the tickets have been sold.
You must show how you get your answer.

(5 marks)

If the question asks you to 'show that' something is true, make sure you show all the steps in your working.

$\frac{1}{4}$ of the child passengers have standard tickets.

Hints

- First, find how many child passengers there are.
- Then, work out how many adult passengers there are.
- You can then work out the number of passengers as a percentage of 200

2 Use the hint below to complete the student's answer so that it would be awarded 2 marks.

16 In a shop, all normal prices are reduced by 10% to give the sale price.
The sale price of a mobile phone is then reduced by 20%.

Selassie says,
"10 + 20 = 30, so the normal price of the mobile phone has been reduced by 30%."

Is Selassie right?
Explain why.

(2 marks)

Hint

- Find the single multiplier that represents a reduction of 10% followed by a reduction of 20%.

100% − 10% = 90% = 0.9

100% − 20% = 80% = 0.8

....

If the question says 'explain', show your working out and then write a sentence or two to answer the question.

Find the answer

1 Find the answer that would be awarded 3 marks. Choose **A**, **B** or **C**. Explain your choice.

18 Claudio and Trayvon buy some identical cupcakes.

Claudio buys 15 of the cupcakes.
The total weight of Claudio's cupcakes is 1080 g.

Trayvon buys 19 of the cupcakes.
Work out the total weight, in kg, of Trayvon's cupcakes.

(3 marks)

I always double check the units before a calculation to see if anything needs converting.

A

1080g ÷ 15 = 72g
19 × 72g = 1368g
1368g ÷ 1000 = 1.368kg

B

1080g ÷ 19 = 56.8g
15 × 56.8g = 852g
852g ÷ 1000 = 0.852kg

C

1080g ÷ 15 = 72g
19 × 72g = 1368g
1368g ÷ 100 = 13.68kg

Answer .... would get 3 marks because ....

....

....

....

2 Find the answer that would be awarded 4 marks. Choose **A**, **B** or **C**. Explain your choice.

13 Javier, Yves and Zac share £6120 between them.
Javier gets 20% more than Yves.
The ratio of the amount of money Yves gets to the amount of money Zac gets is 7 : 5

Work out the amount of money each receives.

(4 marks)

A

100% − 20% = 80%
80% = 0.8
7 × 0.8 = 5.6
5.6 : 7 : 5
17.6 parts = 6120
1 part = 6120 ÷ 17.6
= £347.73
Javier = 5.6 × £347.73
= £1947.29
Yves = 7 × £347.73
= £2434.11
Zac = 5 × £347.73
= £1738.65

B

100% + 20% = 120%
120% = 1.2
7 × 1.2 = 8.4
8.4 : 7 : 5
20.4 parts = 6120
1 part = 6120 ÷ 20.4
= £300
Javier = 8.4 × £300
= £2520
Yves = 7 × £300
= £2100
Zac = 5 × £300
= £1500

C

20% = 0.2
7 × 0.2 = 1.4
1.4 : 7 : 5
13.4 parts = 6120
1 part = 6120 ÷ 13.4
= £456.72
Javier = 1.4 × £456.72
= £2639.41
Yves = 7 × £456.72
= £3197.04
Zac = 5 × £456.72
= £12 283.60

Answer .... would get 4 marks because ....

....

....

....

When I share quantities in a ratio, I always add my answers to make sure they make the total amount.

Mark the answer

1 Use the mark scheme to assign a mark to the answer. Explain your decision.

20 Carlton wants to invest £4500 in a bank for 2 years.

Carlton wants to have as much money as possible at the end of 2 years.

Which bank should he invest his £4500 in?

Bank A	Bank B
Compound interest	Compound interest
4% for year 1	5% for year 1
3.5% for year 2	2.5% for year 2

(4 marks)

£4500 × 1.04 × 1.035 = £4843.80
£4500 × 1.05 × 1.025 = £4843.13

Answer	Notes
Bank A	P1 process to find the interest for Bank A or Bank B for Year 1 e.g. 4500 × 1.04 (= 4680) or 4500 × 1.05 (= 4725) P1 process to find the interest for Bank A or Bank B for Year 2 e.g. 4500 × 1.04 × 1.035 (= 4843.80) or 4500 × 1.05 × 1.025 (= 4843.13) P1 complete process to find the interest for both banks for Year 2 A1 cao

I would award the answer .... out of 4 marks because ....

....

....

....

2 Use the mark scheme to assign a mark to the answer. Explain your decision.

20 Anna has £300, Ben has £140 and Khalil has £100

Anna gives some money to Ben and Khalil. The ratio of the amount of money Anna, Ben and Khalil have now is 4 : 3 : 2

How much money did Ben and Khalil each receive from Anna? **(4 marks)**

4 + 3 + 2 = 9 and £300 + £140 + £100 = £540

Ben = $\frac{3}{9}$ × 540 = 180, Khalil = $\frac{2}{9}$ × 540 = 120

Ben = £180 + £140 = £320 and Khalil = £120 + £100 = £220

Ben £320, Khalil £220

Answer	Notes
Ben £40 and Khalil £20	P1 process to work out the amount of money for Ben or Khalil e.g. $\frac{3}{9} \times 540 (= 180)$ or $\frac{2}{9} \times 540 (= 120)$ P1 complete process to work out the amount of money for Ben and Khalil P1 process to work out the amount of money given to Ben or Khalil e.g. "180" – 140 (= 40) or "120" – 100 (= 20) A1 for 40 and 20

I would award the answer .... out of 4 marks because ....

....

....

....

Re-order the answer

1 Rearrange the working out into the most logical order by numbering each part. Use the hints to help.

21 Rectangle *ABCD* is similar to rectangle *DAXY*.

DC = 15 cm

AD = 6 cm

Work out the difference in area between rectangle *ABCD* and rectangle *DAXY*.

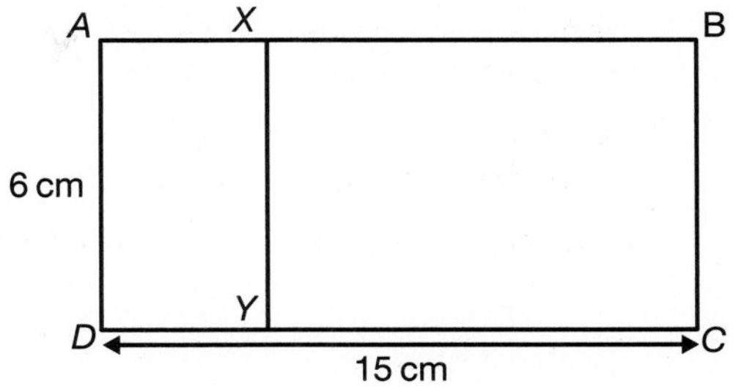

Hints
- First, work out the width of rectangle *DAXY*.
- Then, work out its area.

(3 marks)

☐ $= 75.6\text{ cm}^2$

☐ $2.4 \times 6 = 14.4\text{ cm}^2$

☐ $6 \times \frac{6}{15} = 2.4\text{ cm}$

☐ $(15 \times 6) - 14.4$

2 Rearrange the working out into the most logical order by numbering each part.

16 Lisa is organising a charity event to raise money.
18% of the total money raised will cover the costs of the event.
The rest of the money raised will be given to a care home and to a school in the ratio 5 : 3

Lisa sells 1500 tickets at £39.50 each.

Work out the amount of money that Lisa expects to give to the care home and to the school.
You must show all your working.

(5 marks)

☐ 8 parts = 48 585

☐ 5 parts = 6073.125 × 5 and 3 parts = 6073.125 × 3

☐ 1500 × 39.50 = 59 250

☐ 1 part = 6073.125

☐ 59 250 × 0.82 = 48 585

☐ £30 365.63 and £18 219.38

It can be just as useful to highlight parts of the question in maths and science as it is in English. There's often a lot of information within a short amount of writing.

Complete the question

1 Use the student's working out and answer to complete the question.

7 Two shops have sales.

ABC Clothes	Women's Wear
Sale	Sale
.... % off normal price then .... % off	.... % off normal price

Dorothy wants to buy a dress. The dress has a normal price of £.................

Dorothy wants to buy the dress as cheaply as possible.

Which shop should she buy the dress from?
You must show all your working. **(4 marks)**

Nailed it!

525 × 0.85 = £446.25

446.25 × 0.75 = £334.69

525 × 0.6 = £315

She should buy her dress from Women's Wear because £315 < £334.69

2 Use the student's working out and answer to complete the question.

2 The .... in a .... are ....°, ...°, ...° and ....°.

The angles ...., ... and .... are in the ratio ....

Work out the values of ...., ... and .... **(4 marks)**

Nailed it!

Sum of angles = 360°

360° − 60° = 300°

12 parts = 300°

1 part = 300° ÷ 12 = 25°

$A = 4 \times 25° = 100°$

$B = 5 \times 25° = 125°$

$C = 3 \times 25° = 75°$

$A = 100°$, $B = 125°$, $C = 75°$

Hint

- For what shape has the student worked out the sum of the interior angles?

Complete the answer

1 Use the hint below to complete the student's answer so that it would be awarded 3 marks.

16 Govind has 36 white tiles and 12 black tiles.

The cost of each white tile was £2.50
The cost of each black tile was £4.50

Work out the ratio of the total cost of the white tiles to the total cost of the black tiles.
Give your answer in its simplest form. **(3 marks)**

$36 \times 2.50 = £90$

Hint
- First, find the total cost of the white tiles, and the total cost of the black tiles.

....

2 For each part of the question, complete the student's answer so that it would be awarded full marks.

9 Christine is going to the USA.
She wants to change some pounds to dollars.

A travel agent offers this deal.

Travel Money
Exchange rate: £1 = \$1.35 £10 transaction charge

(a) Write an equation Christine can use to work out how many dollars (*D*) she will get for *P* pounds. **(3 marks)**

Transaction charge in dollars = 10×1.35

....

(b) Christine has £250
How many dollars can she get? **(2 marks)**

Using $D =$

\$ ....

3 Complete the student's answer so that it would be awarded 3 marks.

14 Aiden bought a car for £20000

The value of the car depreciated by 20% in the first year and then by 10% in the second year.

Work out the value of Aiden's car at the end of the two years. **(3 marks)**

End of first year = $20000 \times 0.8 = 16000$

....

Improve the answer

1 Write an improved answer that would be awarded 2 marks.

9 9 calculators cost £40.50
Work out the cost of 16 of these calculators.

The student has correctly started to work out the cost of one calculator, but has made a mistake in their calculation.

(2 marks)

Nearly there

40.50 ÷ 9 = 45.00

16 × 45.00 = £720

........£720........

....

2 Write an improved answer that would be awarded 2 marks.

13 Earl buys a new van for £15 000

The value of the van depreciates at the rate of 24% per year.
After n years the value of the van is £5004.33

Find the value of n.

The student has found the decrease in price for the first year of n but has misunderstood the compound nature of depreciation.

(2 marks)

Had a go

£15 000 × 0.24 = £3600

£15 000 − £3600 − £3600 = £7800

£7800 − £3600 = £4200

........n = 3........

....

3 Write an improved answer that would be awarded 3 marks.

18 Natalia travels to work by train.

The cost of her monthly train ticket increases by 12% to £235.20
Natalia's monthly pay increases by 6% to £535.60

Compare the increase in the amount of money Natalia has to pay for her monthly train ticket with the increase in her monthly pay.

(3 marks)

Had a go

12% of £235.20 = 0.12 × 235.20 = £28.22

6% of £535.60 = 0.06 × 535.60 = £32.14

The monthly pay had a larger increase.

The student has misinterpreted what the amounts in the question represent.

....

Find the answer

1 Find the answer that would be awarded 2 marks. Choose **A**, **B** or **C**. Explain your choice.

6 A box contains only yellow pencils and green pencils.
The ratio of the number of yellow pencils to the number of green pencils is 4 : 11

What fraction of the pencils are yellow? **(2 marks)**

A $\frac{4}{11}$ B $\frac{4}{73}$ C $\frac{4}{15}$

Answer .... would get 2 marks because ....

....

2 Find the answer that would be awarded 2 marks. Choose **A**, **B** or **C**. Explain your choice.

9 Luis has a piece of string that is 180 cm long.
He cuts the string into three lengths in the ratio 3 : 7 : 5

Work out the length, in centimetres, of the longest piece of string. **(2 marks)**

A	B	C
Total parts = 3 + 7 + 5 = 15 $\frac{3}{15} \times 180 = 36$ cm	Total parts = 3 + 7 + 5 = 15 $\frac{7}{15} \times 180 = 84$ cm	Total parts = 3 + 7 + 5 = 15 $\frac{15}{7} \times 180 = 386$ cm

Answer .... would get 2 marks because ....

....

3 Use the hint below to find the answer that would be awarded 3 marks. Choose **A**, **B** or **C**. Explain your choice.

11 Philip is going on holiday to Denmark.
He needs to change some money.

Philip wants to change up to £400 into krone.
He wants as many 50 krone notes as possible.

The exchange rate is £1 = 8.37 krone.
How many 50 krone notes should he get? **(3 marks)**

Hint
- You can assume Philip changes £400

A	B	C
400 × 8.37 = 3348 3348 ÷ 50 = 66.96 67 notes	400 × 8.37 = 3348 3348 ÷ 50 = 66.96 66 notes	400 ÷ 50 = 8 8 × 8.4 = 67.2 67 notes

Answer .... would get 3 marks because ....

....

Complete the question

1 Use the student's working out and answer to complete each part of the question.

14 A scientist is investigating the population growth of a type of bacteria.

At the start of day 1, there are .... bacteria.

The scientist assumes that the population will increase at a constant rate of .... % each day.

(a) Estimate the population of the bacteria at the end of day ....
Give your answer correct to 3 significant figures. **(3 marks)**

Nailed it!

100% + 15% = 115% = 1.15

$50000 \times (1.15)^4 = 87450.3125 = 87500$

......87 500......

The scientist estimates that at the end of day 10 the population of the bacteria will be 202 278

(b) The scientist's assumption about the rate of increase of the population is too ....
How might this affect his estimate for day 10? **(1 mark)**

Hint

- Think about what would happen if the population increased by 10% or 20% each day, for example.

Nailed it!

The population will be less than 202 278 at the end of day 10

2 Use the student's working out and answer to complete the question.

10 Marcel wants to invest £ .... for .... years in a bank.

Penn Bank	WV4 Bank
.... interest .... % for each year	Compound interest .... % for the first year .... % for each extra year

Which bank will give Marcel the most .... at the end of .... years?
You must show all your working. **(3 marks)**

Nailed it!

$35000 \times 1.02^3 = 37142.28$

So 37142.28 − 35000 = £2142.28

$35000 \times 1.042 \times 1.008^2 = 37055.85$

So 37055.85 − 35000 = £2055.85

......Penn Bank......

Mark the answer

1 Use the mark scheme to assign a mark to the answer. Explain your decision.

15 Hassan and Roger are going to share £1250 in the ratio of their ages. The combined age of Hassan and Roger is 24 years. Roger is six years younger than Hassan.

Work out how much money Hassan and Roger each get. You must show all your working. **(5 marks)**

$6 \div 2 = 3$

Hassan's age $= 24 \div 2 + 3 = 12 + 3 = 15$

Roger's age $= 24 \div 2 - 3 = 12 - 3 = 9$

Ratio 15 : 9

Hassan $= \frac{9}{24} \times 1250 = £468.75$

Roger $= \frac{15}{24} \times 1250 = £781.25$

Hassan £468.75, Roger £781.25

If you're sharing in a ratio, add the amounts at the end to check you get the correct total.

Answer	Notes
Hassan £781.25 Roger £468.75	P1 start process to work out the age of Hassan or Roger e.g. $6 \div 2 = 3$ or $24 \div 2 + 3$ (= 15) or $24 \div 2 - 3$ (= 9) P1 complete process to work out the ages of Hassan and Roger e.g. $24 \div 2 + 3$ (= 15) and $24 \div 2 - 3$ (= 9) P1 process to work out the amount of money for Hassan and Roger e.g. $\frac{"15"}{24} \times 1250 (= £781.25)$ or $\frac{"9"}{24} \times 1250 (= £468.75)$ A1 Hassan gets £781.25 A1 Roger gets £468.75

I would award the answer ...... out of 5 marks because ....

....

....

....

2 Use the mark scheme to assign a mark to the answer. Explain your decision.

13 Adele buys a phone for £150 to sell in her shop. At Adele's shop, customers with a loyalty card get 10% off the full price. Adele wants to make a profit of 20% if a customer with a loyalty card buys the phone.
Work out how much Adele should charge for the phone at full price. **(3 marks)**

$150 \times 1.20 = 180$

$180 \div 0.9 = 200$

£200

Answer	Notes
£200	P1 for a process to increase the price using 20% e.g. 150×1.2 (= 180) P1 for a process to increase the price using 10% e.g. "180" $\div 0.9$ A1 cao

I would award the answer ...... out of 3 marks because ....

....

Re-order the answer

1 Rearrange the working out into the most logical order by numbering each part.

5 Melissa wants to buy a table.
She looks on the internet and finds two offers.

UK	**France**
£450	€500
No delivery charge	€20 for delivery

£1 = €1.10

Whose table is cheaper, including the delivery charge?
You must show your working. **(3 marks)**

☐ 450 and 473

☐ 500 + 20

☐ The table from the UK is cheaper.

☐ $520 \div 1.10 = 472.73$

2 Rearrange the working out into the most logical order by numbering each part.

11 There are 240 counters in a box.

Each counter is either red or green.
There are three times as many green counters as red counters in the box.
Jacob takes 30% of the green counters from the box.

Work out the ratio of the number of red counters to the number of green counters now in the box.
Give your ratio in its simplest form. **(3 marks)**

☐ 10 : 21

☐ $0.7 \times 180 = 126$

☐ $\frac{3}{4} \times 240 = 180$

☐ red : green = 1 : 3

☐ 60 : 126

Complete the question

1 Use the student's working out and answer to complete the question.

14 Daniel and Hans share some money.

Daniel receives .... %.

Hans' share is larger than Daniel's share.

Write .... share : .... share as a ratio.

Give your answer in its simplest form. **(2 marks)**

Nailed it!

100% − 30% = 70%

30% : 70%

3 : 7

........3 : 7........

2 Use the student's working out and answer to complete the question.

8 In a fridge, there are .... fruit-based pies.

There are .... times as many .... pies as .... pies and

.... as many key lime pies as .... pies.

How many of each type of pie are there in the fridge? **(3 marks)**

Nailed it!

3 : 1

1 : 0.25

3 : 1 : 0.25 so 12 : 4 : 1

17 parts = 119 so 1 part = 7

Apple = 12 × 7 = 84, cherry = 4 × 7 = 28 and key lime = 1 × 7 = 7

........84 apple, 28 cherry, 7 key lime........

3 Use the student's working out and answer to complete the question.

4 Joan bought a car for £ ....

Each year the value of the car depreciated by .... %.

Work out the value of the car .... years after she bought it. **(3 marks)**

Nailed it!

100% − 15% = 85% = 0.85

£16 000 × 0.85 × 0.85 = £11 560

£ ....11 560........

Complete the answer

1 Use the hints below to complete the student's answer so that it would be awarded 5 marks.

14 Here are the instructions for making a lemon drink.

"Mix 1 part of lemon squash with 5 parts of water."

Katrina is going to make lemon drinks for 30 children.
Each child is going to have 2 lemon drinks.
Each cup holds 300 millilitres of lemon drink.
A one-litre bottle of lemon squash costs £1.50

Hints
- First, work out how much lemon drink Katrina needs.
- Then work out how much of this is lemon squash.

Work out the total cost of the bottles of lemon squash Katrina needs to buy. (1 litre = 1000 millilitres) **(5 marks)**

Number of cups = 30 × 2 = 60

£ ....

2 Use the hint below to complete the student's answer so that it would be awarded 3 marks.

19 Ivanka is going to make some chocolate biscuits.
Here are the ingredients needed to make 8 chocolate biscuits.

Ingredients for 8 chocolate biscuits
50 g butter
25 g sugar
60 g flour
10 g cocoa

Hint
- How many biscuits does Ivanka have enough butter for? What about sugar, flour and cocoa?

Ivanka has:
175 g of butter
200 g of sugar
300 g of flour
60 g of cocoa

Work out the greatest number of chocolate biscuits that Ivanka can make with her ingredients.
You must show your working. **(3 marks)**

Butter = 175 ÷ 50 = 3.5

....

Improve the answer

1 Use the hint below to write an improved answer that would be awarded 2 marks.

7 Here are four graphs.

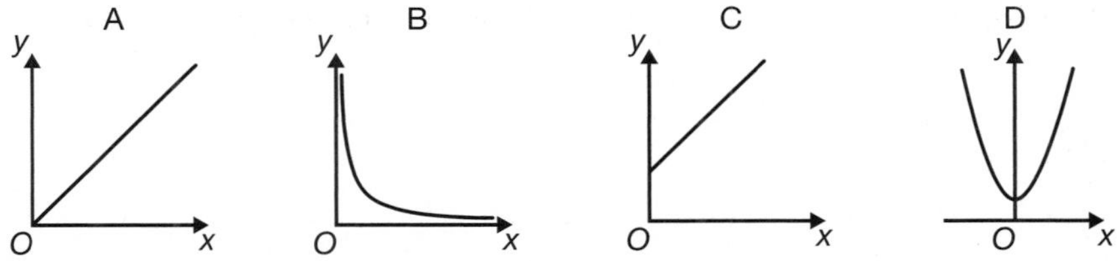

In the table below, match each statement with the letter of its graph. **(2 marks)**

Statement	Graph
A graph showing direct proportion	C
A graph showing indirect proportion	D

Both of the student's answers are incorrect.

Hint
- Think about what happens to the values when they are in direct proportion. What about when one value is 0?

Statement	Graph
A graph showing direct proportion	
A graph showing indirect proportion	

2 Write an improved answer that would be awarded 2 marks.

10 Troy leaves work at 17:55 and arrives at the gym at 18:15
The distance from his work to the gym is 10 miles.

Work out Troy's average speed.
Give your answer in miles per hour. **(2 marks)**

The student has not considered the units they should use for Troy's journey time.

Had a go

$$\text{Speed} = \frac{\text{Distance}}{\text{Time}}$$

$$\text{Speed} = \frac{10}{20} = 0.5$$

0.5 mph

.... mph

Find the answer

1 For each part of the question, find the answer that would be awarded full marks. Choose **A**, **B** or **C**. Explain your choice.

11 Tony uses his van to deliver parcels.
He uses this graph to work out what to charge his customers.

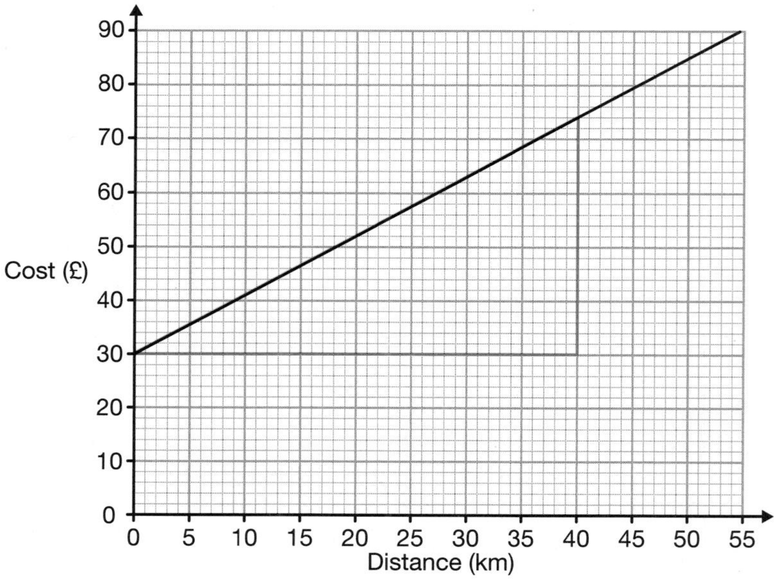

(a) Work out the gradient of the line. **(2 marks)**

A $\text{Gradient} = \frac{40 - 0}{74 - 30} = \frac{40}{44} = 0.909$

B $\text{Gradient} = \frac{40 - 0}{30 - 74} = -0.91$

C $\text{Gradient} = \frac{74 - 30}{40 - 0} = \frac{44}{40} = 1.1$

When drawing a triangle to find a gradient on a graph, try to find points where gridlines intersect.

Answer .... would get 2 marks because ....

....

(b) What does the gradient represent? **(1 mark)**

A For every 1 kilometre travelled, the cost increases by £1.10

B For every 1 kilometre travelled, the cost increases by 91p.

C For every 1 kilometre travelled, the cost increases by 56p.

Answer .... would get the mark because ....

....

Mark the answer

1 Use the mark scheme to assign a mark to the answer. Explain your decision.

15 A tin of beans costs 55p. A shop has a special offer.

Buy 3 tins of beans and get 1 free.

Work out the cost of 20 tins of beans. **(3 marks)**

Tins : free tins = 3 : 1

Number of tins to pay for = $\frac{3}{4} \times 20 = 15$

Cost of the tins = 15 × 55 = 825

£ 825

Answer	Notes
£8.25	P1 process to work out the number of tins e.g. 20 ÷ 4 × 3 (= 15) or (3 + 1) + (3 + 1) + (3 + 1) + (3 + 1) + (3 + 1) = (15 + 5) P1 process to work out the cost of the tins e.g. "15" × 55 (= 825) or "15" × 0.55 (= 8.25) A1 cao

I would award the answer .... out of 3 marks because ....

....

....

2 Use the mark scheme to assign a mark to the answer. Explain your decision.

12 Anders and Ravi share £4800 in the ratio 5 : 7
Anders gives half of his share to Saul.
Ravi gives one quarter of his share to Saul.

Write the ratio of the amount Saul receives to the total amount. Give your answer in its simplest form. **(4 marks)**

Anders = $\frac{5}{12} \times 4800 = 2000$ and Ravi = $\frac{7}{12} \times 4800 = 2800$

2000 ÷ 2 = 1000 and 2800 ÷ 4 = 700

Saul = 1000 + 700 = 1700

Ratio = 1700 : 4800

Answer	Notes
17 : 48	P1 for a process to work out Anders' and Ravi's shares e.g 4800 ÷ 12 × 5 (= 2000) and 4800 ÷ 12 × 7 (= 2800) P1 for a process to work out the amount given to Saul e.g. "2000" ÷ 2 (= 1000) and "2800" ÷ 4 (= 700) P1 for a process to work out the total amount given to Saul e.g. "1000" + "700" = (1700) A1 cao

I would award the answer .... out of 4 marks because ....

....

....

Re-order the answer

1 Rearrange the working out into the most logical order by numbering each part. Use the hint to help.

2 Sophia makes a scale model of a ship.
She uses a scale of 1 : 25
The length of Sophia's model ship is 48 cm.

Cassius makes a scale model of the same ship.
He uses a scale of 1 : 40

What is the difference in length of the two model ships? **(3 marks)**

☐ = 18 cm

☐ 1200 ÷ 40 = 30

☐ 25 × 48 = 1200

☐ 48 − 30

Hint
- First, work out the length of the real ship.

2 Rearrange the working out into the most logical order by numbering each part. Use the hint to help.

13 Here is a map showing Penn and Basingstoke.

1 cm represents 10 km

Nav leaves Penn to travel to Basingstoke. His average speed is 80 km/h.

Work out how long, in minutes, it takes him to travel from Penn to Basingstoke. **(3 marks)**

☐ = 52.5

☐ 7 × 10 = 70

☐ 0.875 × 60

☐ 70 ÷ 80 = 0.875

Hint
- First, use the map to find the distance between Penn and Basingstoke.

Complete the answer

1 Use the hint below to complete the student's answer so that it would be awarded 3 marks.

21 a is inversely proportional to b.
When $b = 18$, $a = 6$

Find the value of a when $b = 16$ **(3 marks)**

$a \propto \frac{1}{b}$

Hint
- Write an equation connecting a and b using k, the constant of proportionality. Solve for k.

....

2 Use the hints below to complete the student's answer so that it would be awarded 3 marks.

11 A box contains red, blue and yellow counters.

The ratio of the number of red counters to the number of blue counters is 7 : 6
The ratio of the number of blue counters to the number of yellow counters is 4 : 3
The total number of counters is 560

How many blue counters are there in the box? **(3 marks)**

7 : 6 = 14 : 12

Hints
- First, rewrite both ratios so that the number of parts representing blue counters is the same.
- You can then combine the two ratios into one three-part ratio.

....

3 Use the hints below to complete the student's answer so that it would be awarded 3 marks.

4 Given that

$4x - 7 : 3 = 2x + 3 : 5$

find the exact value of x. **(3 marks)**

$$\frac{4x-7}{3} = \frac{2x+3}{5}$$

Hints
- Rewrite the ratios as fractions.
- Then, solve the equation to find x.

....

Improve the answer

1 Write an improved answer that would be awarded 3 marks.

19 y is proportional to x.

When $x = 6$, $y = 150$

Work out the value of y when $x = 4$

(3 marks)

Nearly there

$y \propto x$

$y = kx$

$150 = k \times 6$

$k = 6 \div 150$

$k = 0.04$

$y = 0.04x$

$y = 0.04 \times 4$

$y = 0.16$

........0.16........ ....

The student has set up an equation linking x and y, but has made a mistake in their calculation of k.

2 Write an improved answer that would be awarded 3 marks.

9 The diagram shows a solid triangular prism.

The prism is made from metal.

The mass of the metal prism is 924 grams.

Work out the density, in grams per cm^3, of the metal.

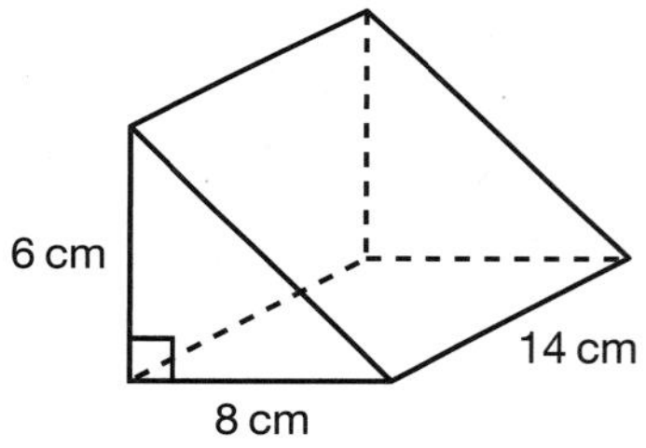

(3 marks)

Nearly there

$$\text{Volume} = \frac{1}{2} \times 6 \times 8 \times 14$$

$$= 336\ cm^3$$

$$\text{Density} = \frac{\text{Volume}}{\text{Mass}}$$

$$= \frac{336}{924} = 0.364$$

........0.364........ g/cm^3 .... g/cm^3

The student has correctly worked out the volume of the prism, but has incorrectly written the formula for density.

Complete the answer

1 Use the hints below to complete the student's answer so that it would be awarded 3 marks.

15 Ian is building a wall.

When he uses 750 bricks, the wall is 6 metres long and 1.25 metres high.
Ian wants the finished wall to be 10 metres long and 1.25 metres high.

How many more bricks does Ian need to finish the wall? **(3 marks)**

1m: 750 ÷ 6 = 125

Hints
- Work out how many bricks Ian uses per metre of wall.
- Then, work out how many bricks Ian needs for the whole wall.
- Finally, work out how many more bricks Ian needs.

....

2 Use the hint below to complete the student's answer so that it would be awarded 4 marks.

8 A shop sells packs of kitchen rolls in three sizes.

A pack of 8 kitchen rolls costs £4.40
A pack of 6 kitchen rolls costs £3.33
A pack of 5 kitchen rolls costs £2.80

Which pack gives the best value for money?
You must show all your working. **(4 marks)**

Hint
- Work out the cost per roll for each pack.

Pack of 8: 440 ÷ 8 = 55p each

....

3 Use the hints below to complete the student's answer so that it would be awarded 3 marks.

12 Gil sells some bags of carrots and bags of turnips at his farm shop.

In one week, he sells three times as many bags of carrots as bags of turnips.
The total number of bags of carrots and bags of turnips he sells is 40

He sells the bags of carrots and bags of turnips for £52 in total. He sells each bag of carrots for £1.15
Work out the cost of each bag of turnips. **(3 marks)**

Carrots : turnips = 3 : 1

Hints
- Work out how many bags of carrots and how many bags of turnips Gil sells.
- Work out the total cost of the bags of carrots Gil sells.
- Then, work out the cost of the turnips.

....

Improve the answer

1 For each part of the question, write an improved answer that would be awarded full marks.

11 (a) Describe fully the single transformation which maps triangle **A** onto triangle **B**. **(3 marks)**

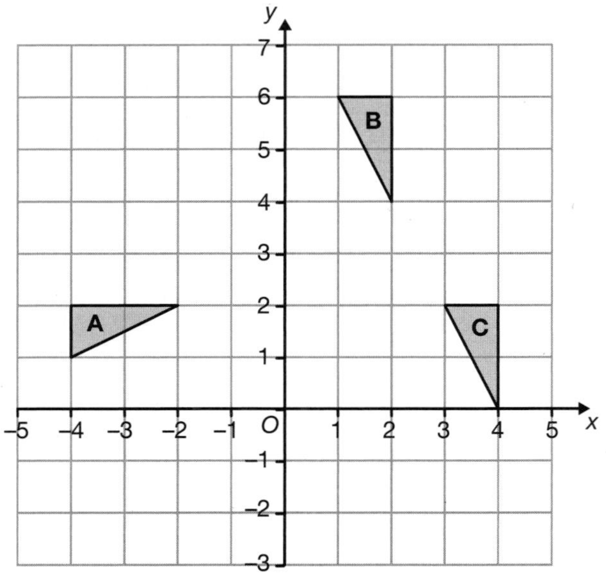

Nearly there

Rotation 90°

The student has correctly identified that this is a rotation of 90°. They have not stated the centre of rotation or the direction.

(b) Describe fully the single transformation which maps triangle **C** onto triangle **B**. **(2 marks)**

Transformation of $\begin{pmatrix} -2 \\ 4 \end{pmatrix}$

The student has used the wrong word to describe the transformation.

2 Write an improved answer that would be awarded 2 marks.

16 Using $\mathbf{a} = \begin{pmatrix} 5 \\ -2 \end{pmatrix}$ and $\mathbf{b} = \begin{pmatrix} 4 \\ 3 \end{pmatrix}$

Work out $\mathbf{b} - 3\mathbf{a}$ **(2 marks)**

Nearly there

$$b - 3a = \begin{pmatrix} 4 \\ 3 \end{pmatrix} - 3\begin{pmatrix} 5 \\ -2 \end{pmatrix} = \begin{pmatrix} 4 - 15 \\ 3 - 6 \end{pmatrix} = \begin{pmatrix} -11 \\ -3 \end{pmatrix}$$

$\begin{pmatrix} -11 \\ -3 \end{pmatrix}$

The student has set the calculation up correctly, but has made a mistake with the signs.

Find the answer

1 Find the answer that would be awarded 2 marks. Choose **A**, **B** or **C**. Explain your choice.

15 Find the size of the angle marked *x*. Give a reason for your answer. **(2 marks)**

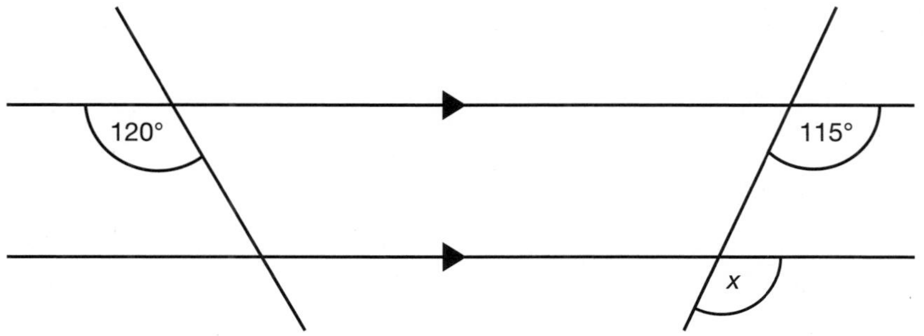

A — 115° because corresponding angles are equal.

B — 120° because corresponding angles are equal.

C — 115° because F angles are equal.

Answer .... would get 2 marks because ....

....

2 Find the answer that would be awarded 2 marks. Choose **A**, **B** or **C**. Explain your choice.

17 *ABC* is a right-angled triangle.

$BC = 12.7$ cm
$AB = 6.9$ cm

Calculate the size of the angle marked *x*.

Give your answer correct to 1 decimal place. **(2 marks)**

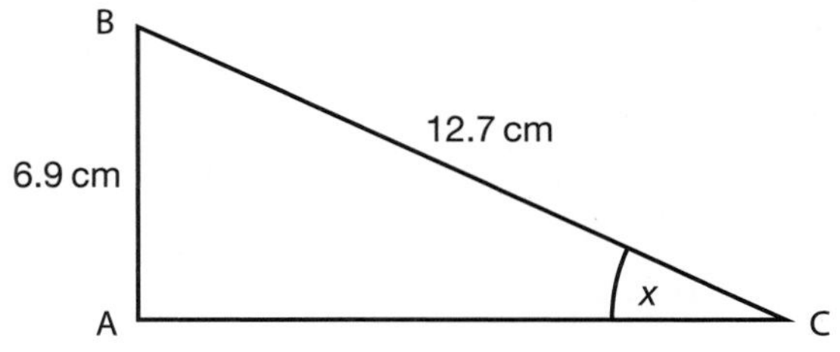

A — $\tan x = \frac{6.9}{12.7}$, $x = 28.5°$

B — $\sin x = \frac{6.9}{12.7}$, $x = 32.9°$

C — $\cos x = \frac{6.9}{12.7}$, $x = 57.1°$

Answer .... would get 2 marks because ....

....

Mark the answer

1 Use the mark scheme to assign a mark to the answer. Explain your decision.

7 A circle has a diameter of 15 cm.

Work out the area of the circle.
Give your answer correct to 3 significant figures. **(2 marks)**

Area = πr^2

$= \pi \times 15 \times 15$

$= 707 \text{ cm}^2$

........707........ cm^2

Answer	Notes
177 cm^2	M1 for $\pi \times 7.5 \times 7.5$ A1 for 177

I would award the answer .... out of 2 marks because ....

....

2 Use the mark scheme to assign a mark to the answer. Explain your decision.

12 Work out the value of x.
Give your answer correct to 3 significant figures. **(4 marks)**

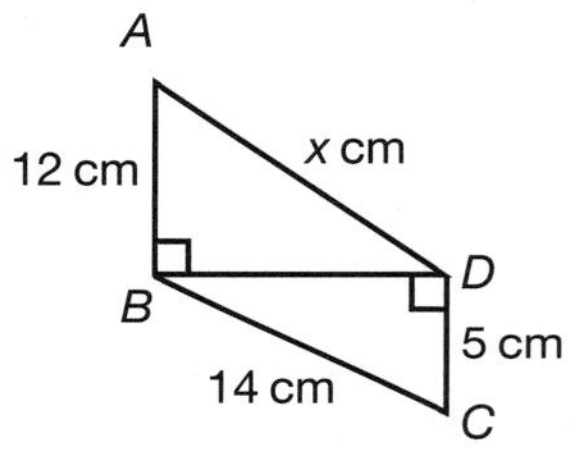

$BD^2 + 5^2 = 14^2$

$BD^2 + 25 = 196$

$BD^2 = 196 - 25$

$BD^2 = 171$

$BD = \sqrt{171}$

$BD = 13.1$

$x^2 = 13.1^2 + 12^2$

$x^2 = 171.61 + 144$

$x^2 = 315.61$

$x = \sqrt{315.61}$

$x = 17.8$

........17.8........ cm

Answer	Notes
17.7	P1 process to find BD^2 e.g. $14^2 - 5^2$ (= 171) P1 process to find x^2 e.g. "171" + 12^2 P1 process to find x e.g. $\sqrt{(\text{"171"}+12^2)}$ A1 cao

I would award the answer .... out of 4 marks because ....

....

....

Re-order the answer

1 Rearrange the working out into the most logical order by numbering each part.

5 The diagram shows a podium in the shape of a circle.

The podium has a diameter of 1.8 m.

Rigby is going to put bunting around the edge of the podium.
The bunting is sold in 0.5 metre rolls.

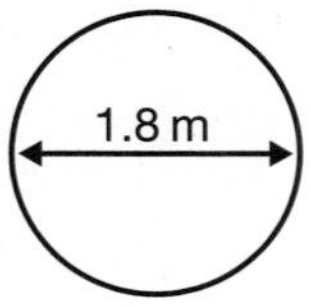

How many rolls of bunting does Rigby need to buy?
You must show all your working. **(3 marks)**

- ☐ = 12
- ☐ $1.8\pi \div 0.5$
- ☐ Length = $\pi \times 1.8$
- ☐ = 11.31

2 Rearrange the working out into the most logical order by numbering each part.

20 *ABCD* is a quadrilateral.

DCE is a straight line.

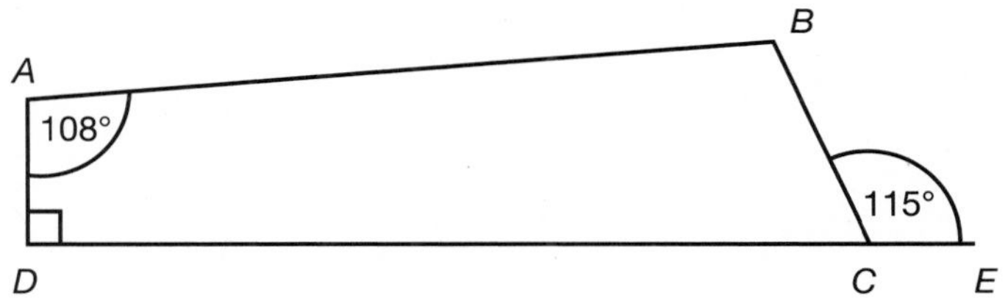

Work out the size of angle *ABC*.

You must give a reason for each stage of your working. **(4 marks)**

- ☐ because angles on a straight line add up to 180°.
- ☐ because angles in a quadrilateral add up to 360°.
- ☐ 180° − 115° = 65°
- ☐ 360° − 90° − 65° − 108° = 97°

Complete the question

1 Use the student's working out and answer to complete the question.

9 The diagram represents a triangular patio *ABC*.

A statue is going to be placed on the patio so that it is:

- nearer to .... than to ....
- within .... metres of point ....

On the diagram, shade the region where the statue may be placed. **(3 marks)**

Nailed it!

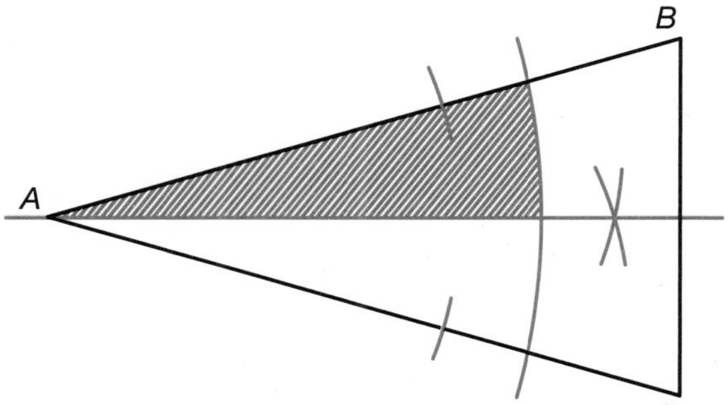

1 cm represents 1 m

2 Use the student's working out and answer to complete the question.

12 The diagram shows a right-angled .... prism **A** and a .... **B**.

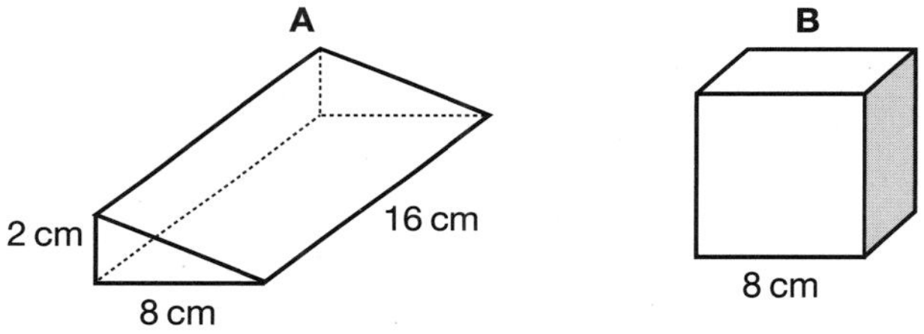

Show that the .... of .... is .... times the .... of .... **(3 marks)**

Nailed it!

$8 \times 8 \times 8 = 512\text{ cm}^3$

$\frac{1}{2} \times 2 \times 8 \times 16 = 128\text{ cm}^3$

$512 = 4 \times 128$

3 Use the student's working out and answer to complete the question.

5 Work out the .... of the .... angles of a .... **(2 marks)**

Nailed it!

Hint
- Think about what you know about angles and polygons.

$(6 - 2) \times 180° = 4 \times 180°$

$= 720°$

.........720.........°

Mark the answer

1 Use the mark scheme to assign a mark to the answer. Explain your decision.

22 The diagram shows the floor plan of a stage.

The floor is in the shape of a rectangle *ABCD* and a semicircle.

CD = 3.4 m
BC = 2.8 m

Sam is going to paint the floor with one coat of paint.

The paint is sold in tins.
One tin will cover 2.25 m^2.
One tin normally costs £18.50

Sam receives a discount of 12% on each tin of paint.
Work out the total cost of the tins of paint.

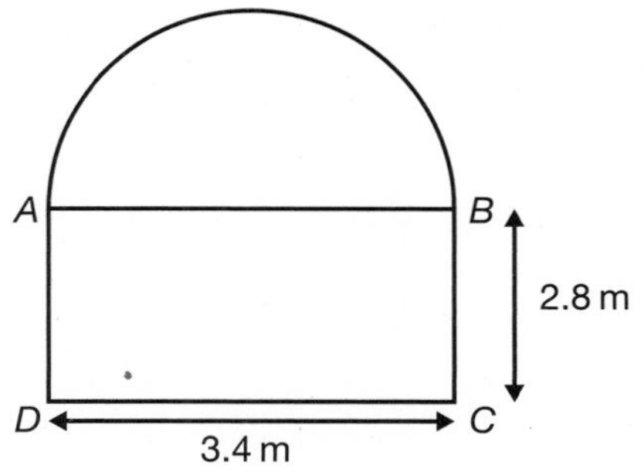

(6 marks)

Radius of circle = 3.4 ÷ 2 = 1.7

Area of semicircle = (π × 1.7 × 1.7) ÷ 2 = 4.5396 = 4.54 m^2

Area of rectangle = 3.4 × 2.8 = 9.52 m^2

Total area = 4.54 + 9.52 = 14.06 m^2

Number of tins = 14.06 ÷ 2.25 = 6.249

12% of £18.50 = 12 ÷ 100 × 18.50 = £2.22

Cost of one tin of paint = 18.50 − 2.22 = £16.28

Total cost = 6 × 16.28 = £97.68

£ ....97.68........

Even if your final answer is wrong, you might still get some method marks so make sure you always show your working.

Answer	Notes
£113.96	P1 process to find the area of the semicircle or circle e.g. π × 1.7 × 1.7 (= 9.079) or (π × 1.7 × 1.7) ÷ 2 (= 4.54) P1 process to find the total area of the stage e.g. "4.54" + (3.4 × 2.8 = (9.52)) (= 14.06) P1 process to find the number of tins e.g. "14.06" ÷ 2.25 (= 6.249) P1 process to find cost of the total number of tins or uses discount to find cost of one tin e.g. "7" × 18.50 or 0.88 × 18.50 P1 process to find total cost e.g. "7" × 18.50 × 0.88 A1 cao

I would award the answer .... out of 6 marks because ....

....

....

....

....

....

Complete the answer

1 Use the hint below to complete the student's answer so that it would be awarded 3 marks.

17 Here is a triangular frame *ABC*.

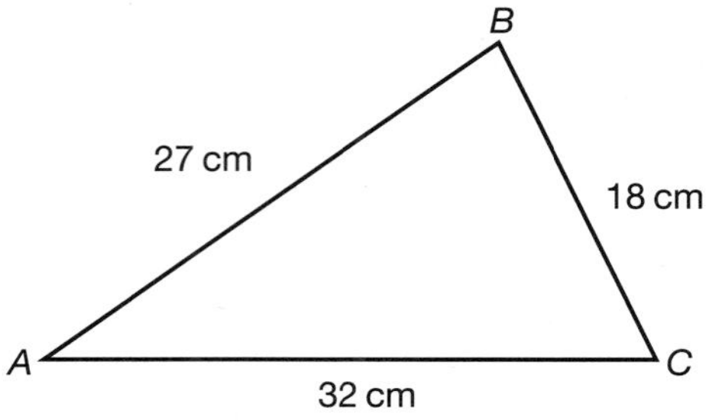

Mario makes a larger, similar triangular frame.
The shortest side is 81 cm.

Work out the total length of wire needed for the larger triangular frame. **(3 marks)**

Hint
- Find the scale factor and apply it to the perimeter of the given triangle.

Scale factor = 81 ÷ 18 = 4.5

.... cm

2 Use the hint below to complete the student's answer so that it would be awarded 3 marks.

16 The diagram shows a quarter of a circle with centre *O* and radius 5.2 cm.

AB is a chord of the circle.

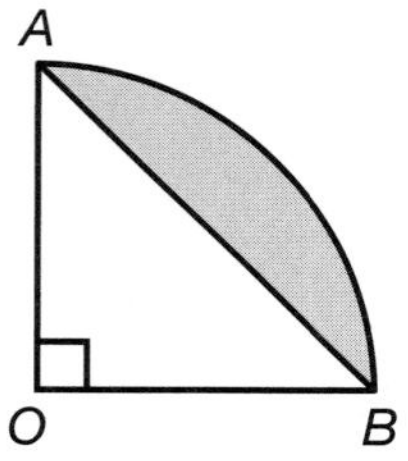

Calculate the area of the shaded segment.

Give your answer correct to 3 significant figures. **(3 marks)**

Hint
- Find the area of the quarter circle and the area of the triangle.

Area of circle = $\pi \times 5.2 \times 5.2 = 84.9487$ cm^2

.... cm^2

I write any measurements on the diagram if they are not already shown.

Improve the answer

1 Write an improved answer that would be awarded 3 marks.

13 Avi is a salesman.

Avi's journey from his home to his office is 75 km.
The journey takes 1 hour 10 minutes.

Work out his average speed in km/h.
Give your answer correct to 3 significant figures. **(3 marks)**

Nearly there

$$\text{Speed} = \frac{\text{Distance}}{\text{Time}}$$

$$= \frac{75}{1.10} = 68.2$$

The student has converted the time Avi's journey takes into hours incorrectly.

......68.2...... km/h

.... km/h

2 For each part of the question, write an improved answer that would be awarded full marks.

14 The diagram shows part of a map.

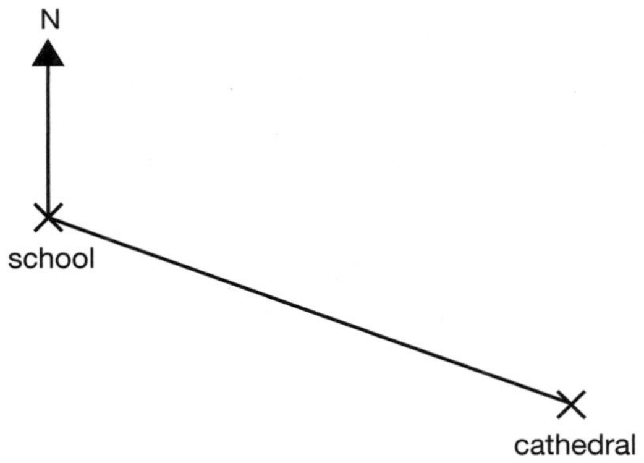

(a) Find the bearing of the cathedral from the school. **(1 mark)**

Had a go

......250...... °

The student appears to have read the wrong scale on their protractor.

.... °

The scale of the map is 1 cm represents 2.5 km.

A shop is 12.5 km due North of the cathedral.

(b) On the diagram, mark the position of the shop with a cross (×).
Label your cross S. **(2 marks)**

$12.5 \times 2.5 = 31.25$ cm

The student has used the scale factor incorrectly and not marked the position of the shop on the map.

Find the answer

1 For each part of the question, find the answer that would be awarded the mark. Choose **A**, **B** or **C**. Explain your choice.

12 The diagram shows a solid triangular prism.

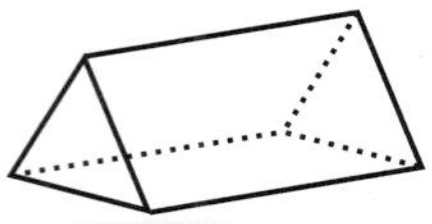

(a) Write down the number of faces. **(1 mark)**

A 5 B 6 C 9

Answer .... would get the mark because ....

....

(b) Write down the number of edges. **(1 mark)**

A 5 B 6 C 9

Answer .... would get the mark because ....

....

(c) Write down the number of vertices. **(1 mark)**

A 5 B 6 C 9

Answer .... would get the mark because ....

....

2 For each part of the question, find the answer that would be awarded the mark. Choose **A**, **B** or **C**. Explain your choice.

13 Here is a quadrilateral.

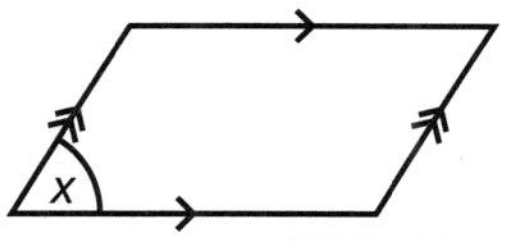

(a) Write down the mathematical name for this shape. **(1 mark)**

A Rectangle B Parallelogram C Rhombus

Answer .... would get the mark because ....

....

(b) Write down the mathematical name for the angle marked *x*. **(1 mark)**

A Acute B Obtuse C Reflex

Answer .... would get the mark because ....

....

Mark the answer

1 Use the mark scheme to assign a mark to the answer. Explain your decision.

19 The diagram shows a **solid** hemisphere.

The diameter of the hemisphere is 12 cm.

Find the total surface area of the solid hemisphere.

Give your answer in terms of π.

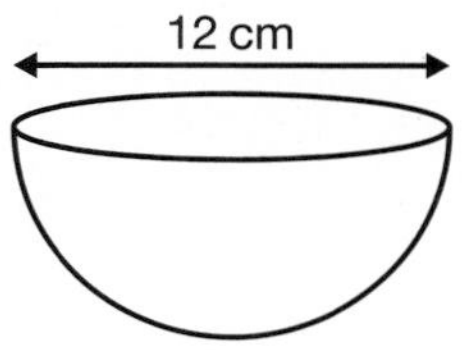

(3 marks)

Surface area = $\frac{4\pi r^2}{2} + \pi r^2 = 3\pi r^2 = 3 \times \pi \times 6^2$

$= 339\text{ cm}^2$

339 cm²

Answer	Notes
108π	M1 for $2\pi r^2 + \pi r^2$ or $3\pi r^2$ M1 for $3 \times \pi \times 6^2$ A1 cao

I would award the answer ...... out of 3 marks because ......

......

......

......

......

2 Use the mark scheme to assign a mark to the answer. Explain your decision.

12 *ABCD* is a parallelogram.

E is the point where the diagonals *AC* and *BD* meet.

Prove that triangle *AED* is congruent to triangle *BEC*.

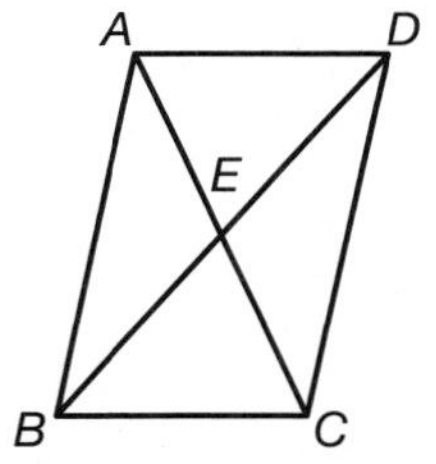

(3 marks)

Angle *BCA* = angle *DAC*

AD = *BC*

Answer	Notes
Complete proof	M1 begins proof that angle *DAC* = angle *BCA* M1 *AD* = *BC* because opposite sides of a parallelogram are equal A1 completes proof e.g. alternate angles are equal and reference to ASA

I would award the answer ...... out of 3 marks because ......

......

......

Find the answer

1 For each part of the question, find the answer that would be awarded the mark. Choose **A**, **B** or **C**. Explain your choice.

13 Here are five triangles drawn on a square grid.

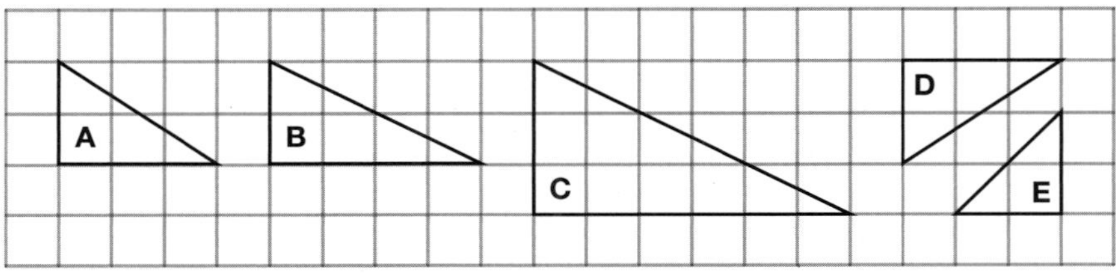

(a) Write down the letters of the two triangles that are congruent. **(1 mark)**

A: A and D   B: D and E   C: B and C

Answer .... would get the mark because ....

....

....

One of the triangles is similar to triangle **B**.

(b) Write down the letter of this triangle. **(1 mark)**

A: A   B: C   C: E

Answer .... would get the mark because ....

....

2 For each part of the question, find the answer that would be awarded the mark. Choose **A**, **B** or **C**. Explain your choice.

5 *A* and *B* are points on a circle.

Write down the mathematical name for

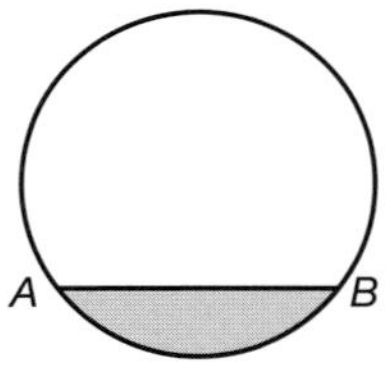

(a) the line *AB*. **(1 mark)**

A: Chord   B: Tangent   C: Diameter

Answer .... would get the mark because ....

....

(b) the shaded region. **(1 mark)**

A: Arc length   B: Sector   C: Segment

Answer .... would get the mark because ....

....

Complete the answer

1 Use the hint below to complete the student's answer so that it would be awarded 2 marks.

10 The diagram shows three points, *A*, *B* and *C*, on a grid.

On the diagram, complete the rectangle *ABCD*. **(2 marks)**

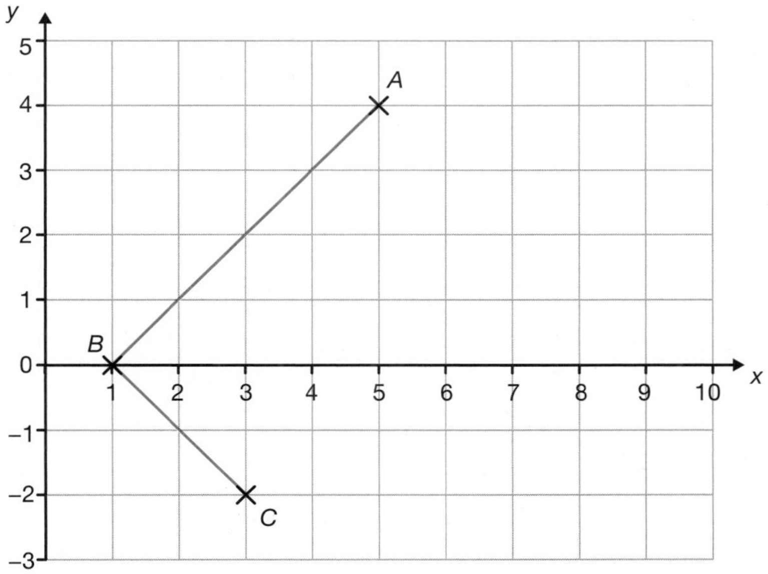

Hint

- Count squares to find the position of point *D*. Don't forget to label it.

2 Use the hint below to complete the student's answer so that it would be awarded 2 marks.

18 The front elevation and the plan for a prism are shown.

Front elevation

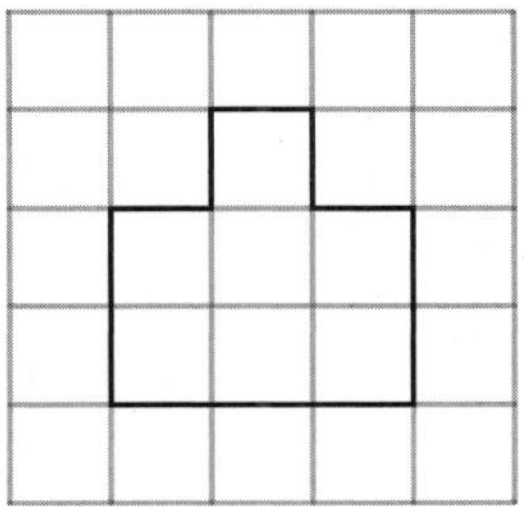

Plan

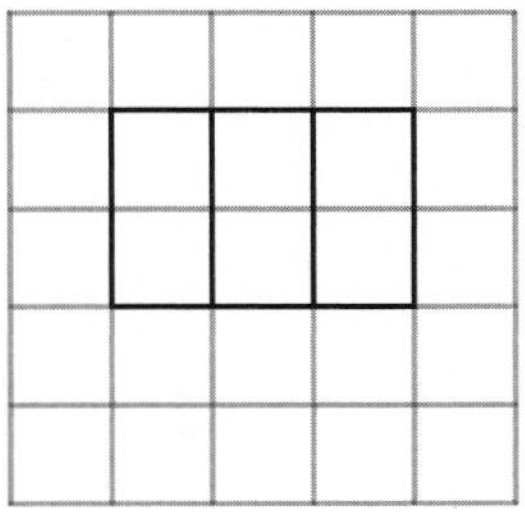

On the grid below, draw the side elevation of the prism. **(2 marks)**

Side

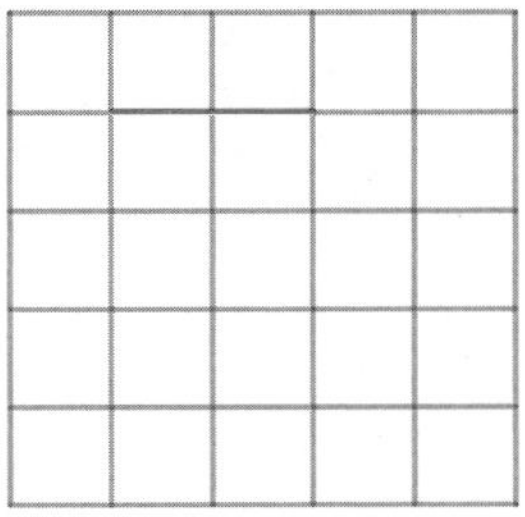

Hint

- Imagine looking at the plan from the side: you can see the shape is 2 squares wide.

Improve the answer

1 For each part of the question, write an improved answer that would be awarded full marks.

10 The table shows the probability that a spinner will land on A, B or C.

Side	A	B	C	D
Probability	0.20	0.35	0.18	27

Nearly there

(a) Work out the probability that the spinner will land on D. **(2 marks)**

0.2 + 0.35 + 0.18 = 0.73

100 − 73 = 27

The student has correctly added the given probabilities, but has then misinterpreted what the result means.

Side	A	B	C	D
Probability	0.20	0.35	0.18	

Celine spins the spinner 250 times.

(b) Work out an estimate for the number of times the spinner will land on A. **(2 marks)**

Had a go

250 ÷ 0.2 = 1250

........1250........ ....

I always read the question again after writing my answer, to check my answer makes sense in context.

2 Write an improved answer to part (b) of the question below that would be awarded 2 marks.

10 Raul plays a game with a fair dice and a spinner.

The spinner is labelled 1, 2, 3 and 4
The dice is labelled 1, 2, 3, 4, 5 and 6

He spins the spinner and throws the dice.
Raul adds the numbers on the spinner to the numbers on the dice to get the total score.

(a) Complete the table to show all the possible total scores. **(1 mark)**

Nailed it!

+	1	2	3	4	5	6
1	2	3	4	5	6	7
2	3	4	5	6	7	8
3	4	5	6	7	8	9
4	5	6	7	8	9	10

(b) What is the probability that Raul's total score will be 8 or more? **(2 marks)**

Nearly there

......6 out of 24......

The student has filled in the table correctly, and identified that there are 6 scores of 8 or more, but has not written the probability in a correct format.

....

Find the answer

1 For each part of the question, find the answer that would be awarded the mark. Choose **A**, **B** or **C**. Explain your choice.

7 Li has a 3-sided spinner.
The sides of the spinner are numbered 10, 20 and 30

(a) Li spins the spinner once.
Write down the word that best describes the probability that the spinner will land on the number 40 **(1 mark)**

A Certain B Even C Impossible

Answer .... would get the mark because ....

....

(b) Write down the word that best describes the probability that the spinner will land on an even number. **(1 mark)**

A Certain B Even C Impossible

Answer .... would get the mark because ....

....

....

2 Find the answer that would be awarded 3 marks. Choose **A**, **B** or **C**. Explain your choice.

6 There are ten coins in a box.
The value of each coin is shown below.

50p	50p	50p	20p	20p	20p	20p	10p	10p	5p

Vince takes a coin from the box at random and keeps it.
Maria then takes a coin from the box at random and keeps it.

Work out the probability that both Vince and Maria take 20p coins. **(3 marks)**

A $\frac{4}{10} \times \frac{4}{10} = \frac{16}{100} = \frac{4}{25}$

B $\frac{4}{10} \times \frac{3}{9} = \frac{12}{90} = \frac{2}{15}$

C $\frac{4}{10} + \frac{3}{9} = \frac{36}{90} + \frac{30}{90} = \frac{66}{90} = \frac{11}{15}$

Answer .... would get 3 marks because ....

....

....

....

Mark the answer

1 Use the mark scheme to assign a mark to the answer. Explain your decision.

3 Jenna recorded the heights, in cm, of 20 shrubs. Show this information in an ordered stem-and-leaf diagram.

(3 marks)

42	49	58	36	56	38	50	41	47	63
34	61	45	58	66	39	68	54	43	66

3	6 8 4 9
4	2 9 1 7 5 3
5	8 6 0 8 4
6	3 1 6 8 6

Answer	Notes
3 | 4 6 8 9 4 | 1 2 3 5 7 9 5 | 0 4 6 8 8 6 | 1 3 6 6 8	B1 for fully correct unordered or ordered with one error or omission B1 for fully correct ordered stem-and-leaf diagram B1 for key

I would award the answer ...... out of 3 marks because ....

....

2 Use the mark scheme to assign a mark to the answer. Explain your decision.

6 Here is a list of numbers

5 9 6 10 11 6 7 4 5

(a) Work out the median. **(2 marks)**

..........11..........

Answer	Notes
6	M1 for ordering the 9 numbers A1 cao

I would award the answer ...... out of 2 marks because ....

....

(b) Work out the mean. **(2 marks)**

5 + 9 + 6 + 10 + 11 + 6 + 7 + 4 + 5 = 63

Mean = 63 ÷ 9 = 7

..........7..........

Answer	Notes
7	M1 for adding all the numbers and dividing by 9 A1 cao

I would award the answer ...... out of 2 marks because ....

....

Re-order the answer

1 Rearrange the working out into the most logical order by numbering each part. One has been done for you.

12 Six numbers are given as 6, 10, 9, 12, 4 and x.

The numbers have a mean of 8
Work out the value of x. **(3 marks)**

- [ ] $48 - 41$
- [ ] $6 + 10 + 9 + 12 + 4 + x = 41$
- [ ] $x = 7$
- [1] $6 \times 8 = 48$

2 Rearrange the working out into the most logical order by numbering each part. Use the hint to help.

5 In a large crate there are some apples, some bananas, some oranges and some pears.

Fruit	Apple	Banana	Orange	Pear
Probability	0.28	0.21	$2x$	x

Jeff takes at random a piece of fruit from the crate.
The table shows the probabilities of taking each type of fruit.

The probability that Jeff will take an orange is twice the probability that he will take a pear.

Work out the probability that Jeff will take an orange. **(3 marks)**

Hint
- The total probability is 1

- [ ] $3x = 0.51$
- [ ] 0.17×2
- [ ] $0.28 + 0.21 + 2x + x = 1$
- [ ] $= 0.34$
- [ ] $x = 0.17$
- [ ] $0.49 + 3x = 1$

Complete the question

1 Use the student's answers and working out to complete the question.

6 There are 200 counters in a bag.

.... of the counters are red.

.... of the counters are blue.

.... of the counters are white.

Raj takes at random a counter from the bag.

Work out the .... that he picks the following.

(a) a red counter **(1 mark)**

Nailed it!

P(red) = $\frac{3}{5}$

$\frac{3}{5}$ ....

(b) a red or blue counter **(2 marks)**

Nailed it!

P(red or blue) = $\frac{3}{5} + \frac{1}{4} = \frac{17}{20}$

$\frac{17}{20}$ ....

(c) a white counter **(1 mark)**

Nailed it!

P(white) = $\frac{3}{20}$

$\frac{3}{20}$ ....

2 Use the student's answer to complete the question.

16 $\mathscr{E}$ = {............... numbers less than 24}

A = {.........,.........,.........,.........,.........}

B = {.........,.........,.........,.........}

Complete the .... diagram to represent this information. **(4 marks)**

Nailed it!

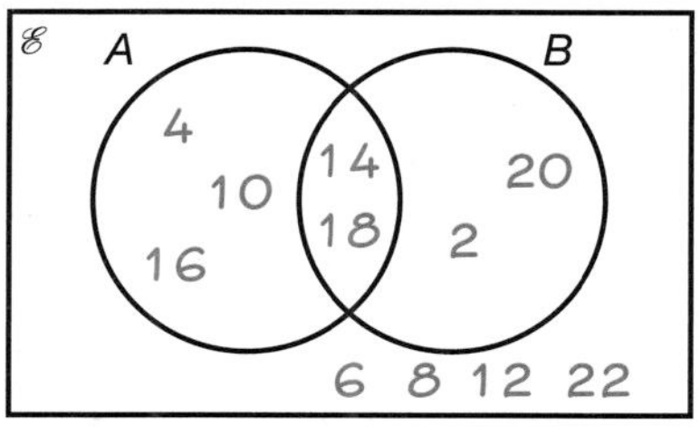

Complete the answer

1 Use the hint below to complete part (b) of the student's answer so that it would be awarded 3 marks.

19 Lea asked each person in her year group how many cars their family has.
The frequency table shows the results.

Number of cars	0	1	2	3	4
Frequency	7	18	12	9	4

(a) Write down the mode. **(1 mark)**

........1........

(b) Work out the mean number of cars. **(3 marks)**

$(0 \times 7) + (1 \times 18) + (2 \times 12) + (3 \times 9) + (4 \times 4)$

....

Hint
- First, work out the total number of cars, and the total number of people asked.

2 For each part of the question, complete the student's answer so that it would be awarded full marks.

3 Asha and Pam are in the same class.

The probability that Asha arrives on time is 0.6
The probability that Pam arrives on time is 0.8

(a) Complete the probability tree diagram. **(2 marks)**

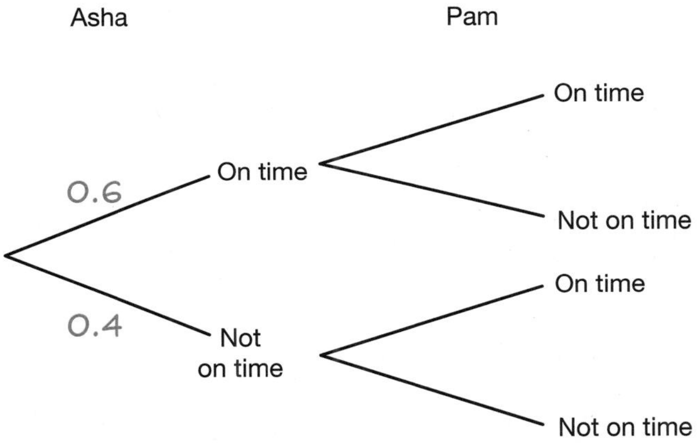

Hint
- Whether Asha is on time does not affect whether Pam is on time – the events are independent.

(b) Work out the probability that they are both on time. **(2 marks)**

P(Asha on time and Pam on time)

....

Hint
- Read along the branches of the probability tree diagram and multiply.

(c) Work out the probability that only one of Asha or Pam is on time. **(2 marks)**

P(Asha on time and Pam not on time) or
P(Asha not on time and Pam on time)

....

Hint
- Add together P(Asha on time and Pam not on time) and P(Asha not on time and Pam on time).

Improve the answer

1 For each part of the question, write an improved answer that would be awarded full marks.

20 The scatter graph shows information about the height and the arm length of seven boys.

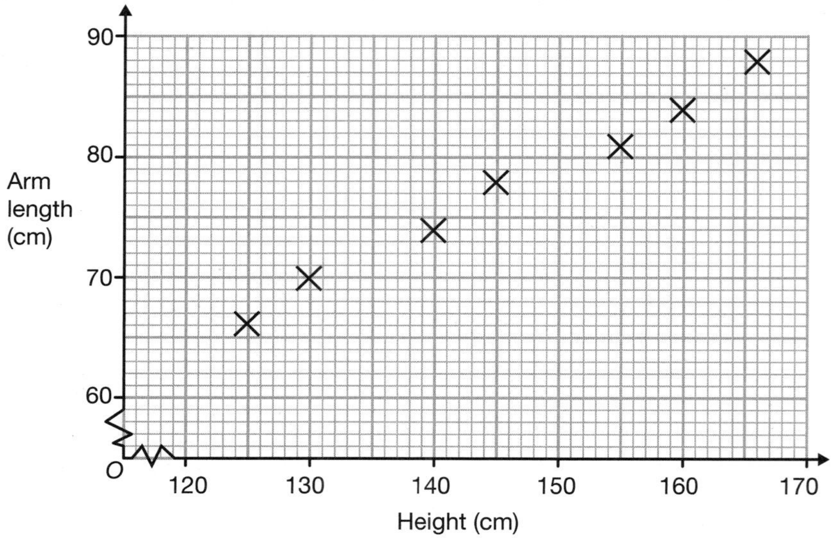

(a) Describe the relationship between the height and arm length of the boys. **(1 mark)**

Had a go

It is going up.

> The student needs to refer to the context of the question in their answer.

Another boy has a height of 135 cm.

(b) Estimate the arm length of this boy. **(2 marks)**

> Questions like this will allow a range of 1 cm above or below the given answer.

Hint
- The student has not used a line of best fit. You should use a line of best to help you estimate the boy's arm length.

Had a go

79 cm   cm

2 Write an improved answer that would be awarded the mark.

3 Simone made the pictogram below to show the number of televisions sold at her shop on a Monday and on a Tuesday.

Monday	○ ○ ○
Tuesday	○ ◗

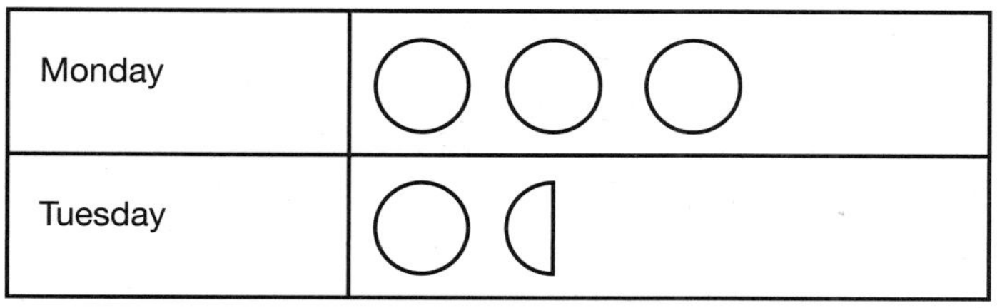

Key: ○ represents 5 televisions

Write down **one** thing that is wrong with this pictogram. **(1 mark)**

Nearly there

Half of a circle has been drawn for Tuesday.

> The student needs to explain why this is a problem.

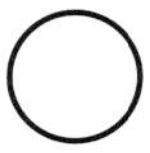

Find the answer

1 For each part of the question, find the answer that would be awarded the mark. Choose **A**, **B** or **C**. Explain your choice.

13 Ray rolls an ordinary fair dice.

(a) On the probability scale, mark with a cross (×) the probability that the dice will land on a number greater than 6 **(1 mark)**

A
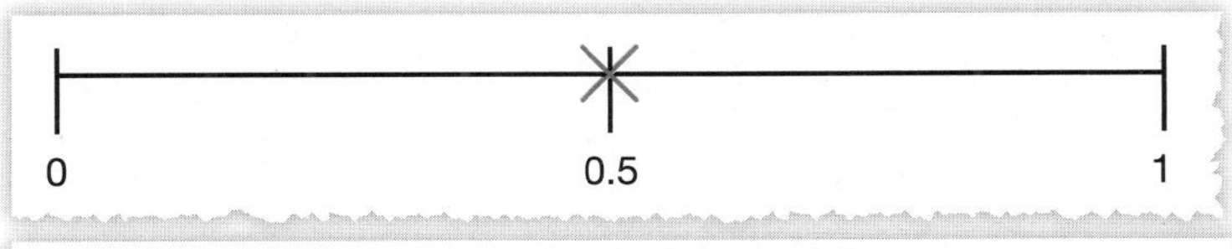

B
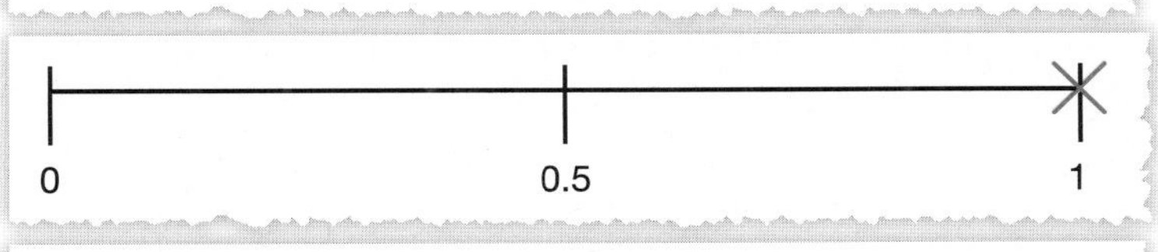

C
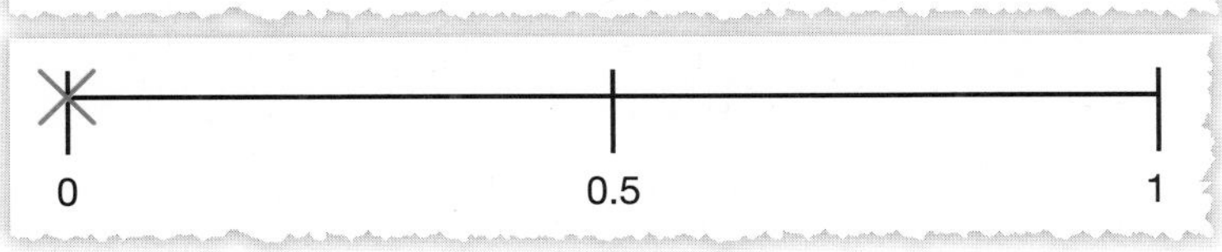

Answer .... would get the mark because ....

....

(b) On the probability scale, mark with a cross (×) the probability that the dice will land on an odd number. **(1 mark)**

A
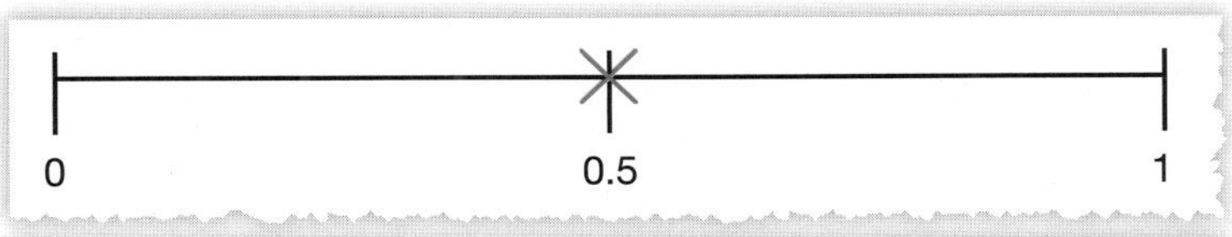

B
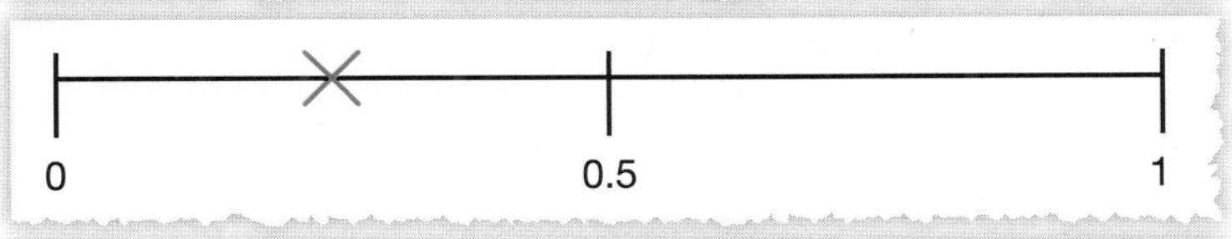

C
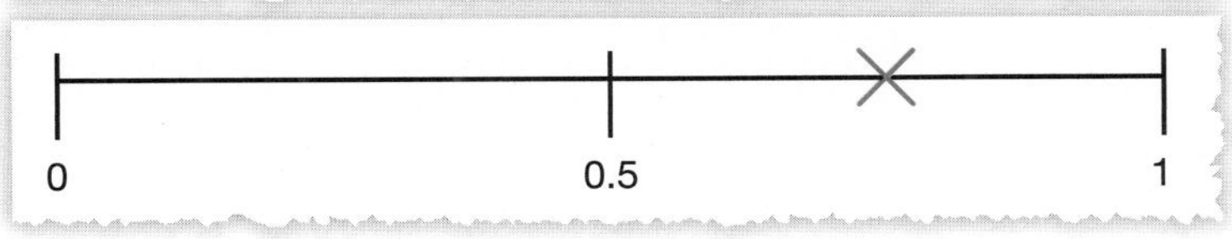

Answer .... would get the mark because ....

....

2 Find the answer that would be awarded the mark. Choose **A**, **B** or **C**. Explain your choice.

8 Here is a fair 6-sided spinner.

Bob is going to spin the spinner once.

Which number is the spinner least likely to land on?

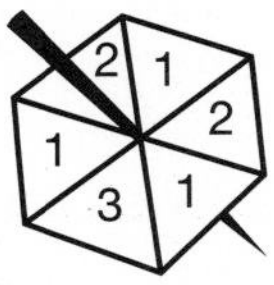

(1 mark)

A 1 B 2 C 3

Answer .... would get the mark because ....

....

Mark the answer

1 Use the mark scheme to assign a mark to the answer. Explain your decision.

19 Maxine is doing a survey to find out how much time students spend playing on their mobile phones.

She is going to ask the first 10 girls on the register for her form class.

This may **not** produce a good sample for Maxine's survey. Give **two** reasons why. **(2 marks)**

The number of girls she is asking is too small and she is only asking girls. ....

Answer	Notes
2 correct reasons	B1 for one acceptable reason from bias relating to gender/bias relating to age/bias relating to form class/sample size is too small/sampling is not random B1 for second acceptable reason from bias relating to gender/bias relating to age/bias relating to form class/sample size is too small/sampling is not random

I would award the answer .... out of 2 marks because ....

....

2 Use the mark scheme to assign a mark to the answer. Explain your decision.

21 The table shows information about annual turnover of a company.

Year	Turnover (£ millions)
2009	17
2010	15
2011	13
2012	10
2013	8
2014	7
2015	5

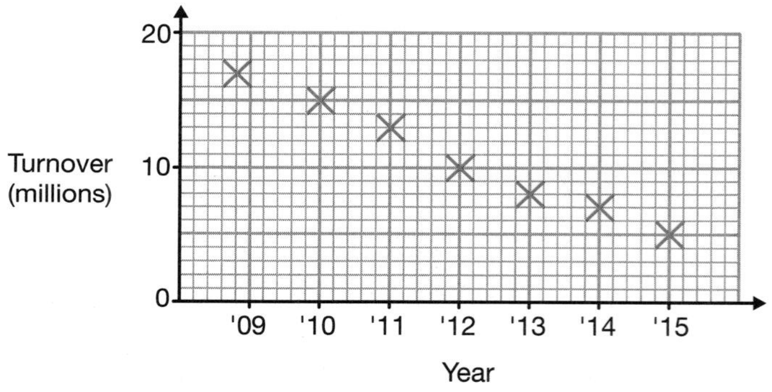

(a) Draw a time series graph to represent this data. **(2 marks)**

Answer	Notes
All points plotted correctly	C1 for at least 5 points plotted correctly C1 for all points plotted correctly (half a square tolerance)

I would award the answer .... out of 2 marks because ....

....

....

(b) Write down the type of correlation. **(1 mark)**

Downwards ....

Answer	Notes
negative	B1 for negative

I would award the answer .... out of 1 mark because ....

....

Improve the answer

1 Write an improved answer that would be awarded 4 marks.

19 Amy asked 40 friends how many minutes they took to get to work.
The table shows her results.

Time taken (t minutes)	Frequency
$0 < t \leqslant 10$	7
$10 < t \leqslant 20$	9
$20 < t \leqslant 30$	12
$30 < t \leqslant 40$	8
$40 < t \leqslant 50$	4

Work out an estimate for the mean time taken. **(4 marks)**

Nearly there

$(10 \times 7) + (20 \times 9) + (30 \times 12) + (40 \times 8) + (50 \times 4)$

$= 70 + 180 + 360 + 320 + 200$

Mean $= 1130 \div 40 = 28.25$

The student has not used the midpoints to estimate the mean.

28.25

....

2 Use the hint below to write an improved answer that would be awarded the mark.

12 The pie charts give information about the types of drinks some boys and girls prefer.

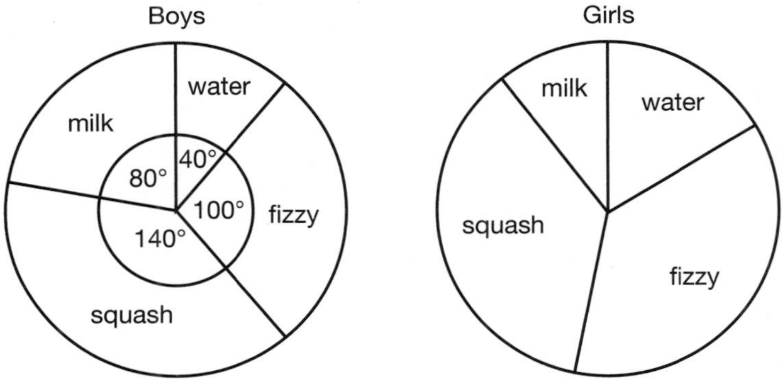

Ang says, "More girls than boys prefer fizzy drinks."
He could be **wrong**.
Explain why. **(1 mark)**

Had a go

The pie chart does not show the angles for the girls.

Hint

- Think about what you would need to know in order to decide whether Ang's statement is true.

....

....

Answers

Improve the answer

1 Use the hint to write an improved answer that would be awarded 2 marks.

14 Tom goes to a restaurant.
He can choose from three types of burgers and three types of side dishes.

Tom is going to choose one burger and one side dish.

List all the possible combinations Tom can choose. **(2 marks)**

Burger	Side
Beef	Salad
Veggie	Fries
Chicken	Potatoes

Hint
- Use letters for the options. For example, use B for 'beef'.

Nearly there

BS, BF, BP, VS, VF, VP, CS, CF, CP, SB, SV, SC, FB, FV, FC, PB, PV, PC

The student has written too many combinations.

BS, BF, BP, VS, VF, VP, CS, CF, CP

2 For each part of the question, write an improved answer that would be awarded full marks.

11 $A = 52000$ and $B = 3 \times 10^3$
Giving your answers in standard form, work out:

(a) $A + B$ **(2 marks)**

Hint
- To answer parts (a) and (b), work with ordinary numbers. Then, convert to standard form at the end.

Had a go

$5.2 \times 10^4 + 3 \times 10^3 = 8.2 \times 10^6$

8.2×10^6

$52000 + 3000 = 55000 = 5.5 \times 10^4$

5.5×10^4

(b) AB **(2 marks)**

Nearly there

The student's final answer is not in standard form.

$5.2 \times 10^4 \times 3 \times 10^3 = 15.6 \times 10^7$

15.6×10^7

$5.2 \times 10^4 \times 3 \times 10^3 = 15.6 \times 10^7 = 1.56 \times 10^8$

1.56×10^8

3 Write an improved answer to each part of the question that would be awarded full marks.

4 Write the following numbers to the stated degree of accuracy.

(a) 0.07483 correct to three decimal places. **(1 mark)**

Had a go

0.0748

0.075

(b) 0.07483 correct to three significant figures. **(1 mark)**

Had a go

0.075

0.0748

The student has confused the meanings of 'decimal places' and 'significant figures'.

Find the answer

1 For each part of the question, find the answer that would be awarded the mark. Choose **A**, **B** or **C**. Explain your choice.

6 (a) Write 0.00541 in standard form. **(1 mark)**

A 5.41×10^3 B 0.541×10^{-2} C 5.41×10^{-3}

Answer C would get the mark because 5.41 is between 1 and 10, and the student has written the power correctly (it is a very small number so it has to be negative).

(b) Write 4.2×10^5 as an ordinary number. **(1 mark)**

A 420000 B 4200000 C 0.000042

Answer A would get the mark because the student has correctly moved the digits five places to the left.

2 Use the hint below to find the answer that would be awarded 2 marks. Choose **A**, **B** or **C**. Explain your choice.

4 Ram buys a computer.
He pays £960 including VAT at 20%.
Work out the price of the computer without the VAT. **(2 marks)**

Hint
- Use the context of the question to check your answer makes sense – think about whether your answer should be more or less than the number given in the question.

A	B	C
20% of £960 = $\frac{20}{100} \times 960$ = £192 Price without VAT = £960 − £192 = £768	Let 120% = £960 1% = $\frac{960}{120}$ 100% = $\frac{960}{120} \times 100$ Price of computer = £800	Multiplier = 100% − 20% = 80% 80% ÷ 100 = 0.8 Price of computer = £960 ÷ 0.8 = £1200

Answer B would get 2 marks because the student has correctly added 20% to 100% and concluded that 120% is equivalent to £960. The student has carried out the correct steps to obtain the final answer.

Mark the answer

1 Use the mark scheme to assign a mark to the answer.

Remember to find a common denominator before adding or subtracting fractions.

5 Work out $5\frac{3}{4} + \frac{7}{9}$
Give your answer as a mixed number in its simplest form. **(3 marks)**

$5\frac{3}{4} + \frac{7}{9} = 5 + \frac{3}{4} + \frac{7}{9}$

$= 5 + \frac{27}{36} + \frac{28}{36} = 5\frac{55}{36}$

$5\frac{55}{36}$

Answer	Notes
$6\frac{19}{36}$	M1 for converting both fractions to get a common denominator of a multiple of 36, with at least one of the fractions correctly converted. M1 (dep on M1) for $5 + \frac{"27"}{36} + \frac{"28"}{36} \left(= 5\frac{55}{36}\right)$ A1 cao

I would award the answer 2 out of 3 marks because the student has correctly found a common denominator of 36 and has successfully added the fractions, gaining the first two marks. The student does not get the third mark because they haven't converted the improper fraction.

2 Use the mark scheme to assign a mark to the answer.

12 There are 75 students in a school. The school organises three trips. Each student can choose to go on one trip.
They can go to a theme park, a castle or a zoo.

25 students choose the zoo.
40 students are girls.
15 girls choose the theme park.
17 boys choose the theme park.
Equal numbers of boys and girls choose the castle.

Complete the two-way table. **(3 marks)**

When I fill in a two-way table, I always check all the totals in the table match the totals in the question.

	Theme park	Castle	Zoo	Total
Girls	15	8	17	40
Boys	17	8	10	35
Total	32	18	25	75

Answer	Notes
15, 9, 16, 40 17, 9, 9, 35 32, 18, 25, 75	B1 for 15, 17, 25, 40, 75 B1 for 32 or 35 or 18 B1 for all correct entries

I would award the answer 2 out of 3 marks because the student has correctly filled in all the numbers given in the question and worked out the other three totals, gaining the first two marks. They don't get full marks because they have made a numerical error working out the numbers for the castle, so the numbers for the zoo are also wrong.

Re-order the answer

1 Rearrange the working out into the most logical order by numbering each part. Use the hint to help.

6 Every evening, Diane cycles the same distance.
One evening, she stops for a rest when she has cycled exactly half the distance.
After a further 3 km, she has cycled exactly $\frac{5}{8}$ of the total distance.
How many kilometres does Diane cycle each evening? You must show your working. **(3 marks)**

Hint
- First, work out what fraction of the distance 3 km represents.

[5] = 24

[3] $\frac{1}{8}$ is equivalent to 3 km

[1] $\frac{5}{8} - \frac{1}{2}$

[4] 3 × 8

[2] $= \frac{5}{8} - \frac{4}{8} = \frac{1}{8}$

2 Rearrange the working out into the most logical order by numbering each part.

12 In January, Rob received £1500 commission on sales he had made that month.
In February, he received 20% less commission than he did in January.
In March, his commission was 15% higher than it was in February.
In April, his commission was 30% higher than it was in March.
How much commission did Rob receive in April? **(3 marks)**

[3] £1380 × 1.30

[1] £1500 × 0.8

[4] = £1794

[2] £1200 × 1.15

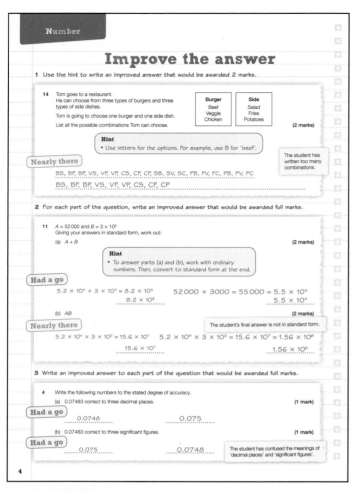

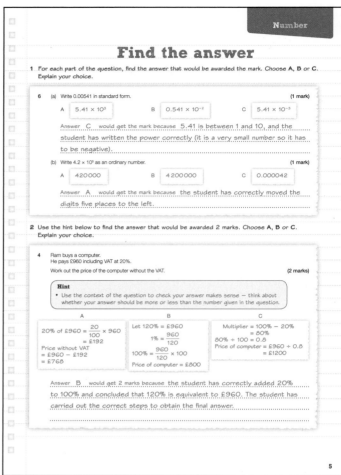

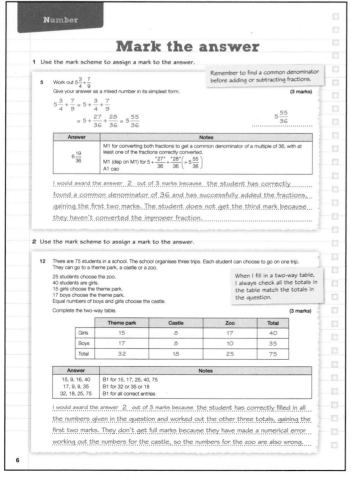

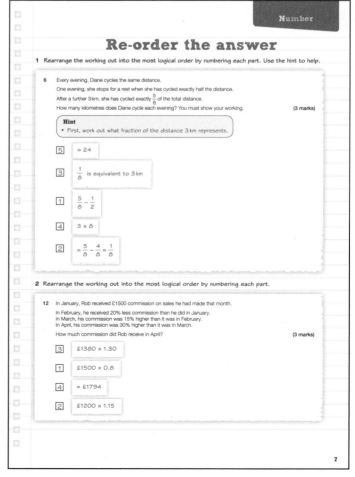

Complete the question

1 Use the student's answers to complete each part of the question.

Hint
- Write the missing power in the box.

5 (a) Write down the value of 9^{0} (1 mark)

Nailed it!

1

(b) Write down the value of 9^{-2} (1 mark)

Nailed it!

$\frac{1}{81}$

(c) Write down the reciprocal of $\frac{4}{9}$ (1 mark)

Nailed it!

$\frac{9}{4}$

2 Use the working out to complete the question.

3 Sandeep has 180 counters.
All of the counters are blue, yellow, green or red.
25% of the counters are blue.
$\frac{1}{3}$ of counters are yellow.
The ratio of the number of green counters to the number of red counters is 3 : 2
Work out the number of red counters. (5 marks)

Nailed it!

This question tests your knowledge of ratio and proportion as well as your number skills.

25% of 180 = 0.25 × 180 = 45
$\frac{1}{3} \times 180 = 60$
45 + 60 = 105
180 − 105 = 75
$\frac{2}{5} \times 75 = 30$

30

3 Use the student's answer to complete the question.

Make sure you understand the key mathematical terms you have learnt.

4 A number, n, is rounded to 2 decimal places.
The result is 6.17
Using inequalities, write down the error interval for n. (2 marks)

Nailed it!

$6.165 \leq n < 6.175$

Complete the answer

1 For each part of the question, complete the student's answer so that it would be awarded full marks.

6 Gunnar orders some groceries. His shopping bill is shown.

3 cartons of juice at £1.45 each	£4.35
4 bottles of milk at 94p each	£3.76
1 loaf of bread	£1.25
5 bread rolls at 18p each	£0.90
2 blocks of cheese at £2.35 each	£4.70
Order total	£14.96
Delivery charge	£2.50
Total amount to pay	£17.46

Hints
- Read each line of the receipt carefully.
- Write all of your answers in pounds.

(a) Fill in the missing amounts. (3 marks)
(b) Gunnar pays with a £20 note.
How much change should he receive? (2 marks)

£20 − total amount = amount of change received
£20 − £17.46 = £2.54

£ 2.54

2 Complete the student's answer so that it would be awarded 4 marks.

15 A car costs £9950 before a sale. In the sale, the price is reduced by 12%.
Helga buys the car during the sale.
She puts down a deposit of £3422
She will pay off the rest of the cost in 24 equal payments.
How much is each payment?
You must show all your working. (4 marks)

Read the question carefully and underline key words.

100% − 12% = 88%
0.88 × £9950 = £8756
£8756 − £3422 = £5334
£5334 ÷ 24 = £222.25

£ 222.25

Improve the answer

1 Write an improved answer that would be awarded 2 marks.

7 Work out an estimate for the value of $\frac{4.93 \times 306}{0.5023}$ (2 marks)

Nearly there

$\frac{5 \times 300}{1} = \frac{1500}{1} = 1500$

1500

$\frac{5 \times 300}{0.5} = \frac{1500}{0.5} = \frac{3000}{1} = 3000$

3000

When estimating, I usually round each number to 1 significant figure.

2 Write an improved answer that would be awarded 4 marks.

16 Andrea works in a shop.
Her normal rate of pay is £8 per hour.
When Andrea works more than 7 hours a day, she is paid an overtime rate for each hour she works after the first 7 hours.
Andrea's rate of overtime pay per hour is $1\frac{1}{4}$ times her normal rate of pay per hour.
On Saturday Andrea worked for 11 hours.
She thinks that she should have earned more than £100 on this Saturday.
Is she correct?
You must show your working. (4 marks)

Had a go

$\frac{1}{4}$ of £8 = £2
Overtime rate = £8 + £2 = £10
Total pay = 11 × £10
= £110

Yes, she has earned more than £100.

The student has incorrectly applied the overtime rate to all the hours worked.

Pay for 7 hours = 7 × 8 = £56
$\frac{1}{4}$ of £8 = £2
Overtime rate = £8 + £2 = £10
Number of hours overtime worked = 11 − 7 = 4
Overtime pay = 4 × £10 = £40
Total pay = £56 + £40
= £96

No, she has not earned more than £100

Find the answer

1 For each part of the question, find the answer that would be awarded the mark. Choose A, B or C. Explain your choice.

3 (a) Write the number forty thousand and sixty-three in digits. (1 mark)

A 40630 B 40063 C 4063

Answer B would get the mark because the student has correctly written the digits according to their place value.

(b) Write down the value of the 5 in the number 745 638 (1 mark)

A 5000 B 50000 C 500

Answer A would get the mark because the student has correctly identified that the number 5 is in the thousands column.

2 Find the answer that would be awarded the mark. Choose A, B or C. Explain your choice.

5 Work out the value of 2^5 (1 mark)

A 2 + 2 + 2 + 2 + 2 = 10 B 2 × 5 = 10 C 2 × 2 × 2 × 2 × 2 = 32

Answer C would get the mark because the student has correctly identified that the power 5 means that 2 is multiplied by itself five times.

3 Find the answer that would be awarded the mark. Choose A, B or C. Explain your choice.

1 Write $\frac{4}{5}$ as a percentage. (1 mark)

A $\frac{4}{5} \times 100 = 0.8 \times 100 = 80\%$ B $\frac{4}{5} \times 100 = 0.8 \times 100 = 8\%$ C $\frac{4}{5} = 0.8$

Answer A would get the mark because the student has correctly multiplied by 100 to work out the percentage.

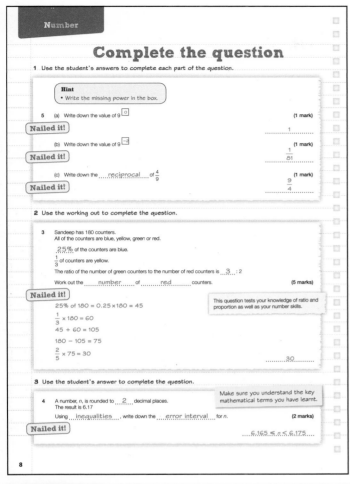

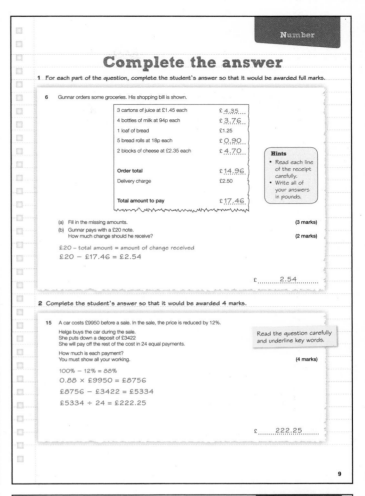

Re-order the answer

1 Rearrange the working out into the most logical order by numbering each part. Use the hint to help.

3 Work out $3\frac{4}{5} - 1\frac{2}{3}$

Give your answer as a mixed number. **(3 marks)**

Hints
- Work out the answer for yourself.
- Compare this working with your own.

4 $= 2\frac{2}{15}$

1 $= \frac{19}{5} - \frac{5}{3}$

3 $= \frac{32}{15}$

2 $= \frac{57}{15} - \frac{25}{15}$

2 Rearrange the working out into the most logical order by numbering each part.

13 The price of a television is reduced by 15% in a sale.
The sale price of the television is £765
Work out the price of the television before the sale. **(3 marks)**

This question tests your knowledge of proportion as well as your number skills.

4 100% = £9 × 100

1 100% − 15% = 85%

5 100% = £900

2 85% = £765

3 1% = £765 ÷ 85 = £9

Complete the question

1 Use the student's answers to complete each part of the question.

3 Here is a list of numbers

2 7 12 16 22 27

Hint
- Think about what **types** of numbers the answers are.

From the numbers in the list, write down:

(a) the ....square.... number **(1 mark)**

Nailed it! ....16....

(b) the ....cube.... number **(1 mark)**

Nailed it! ....27....

(c) the ....prime.... numbers. **(1 mark)**

Nailed it! ....2 and 7....

2 Use the student's working out and answer to complete the question.

16 ..4.. spheres have a total weight of ..1400.. grams.
..5.. spheres and ..3.. cubes have a total weight of ..2200.. grams.
Work out the total weight, in grams, of ..3.. spheres and ..2.. cubes. **(4 marks)**

Nailed it!

1400 g ÷ 4 = 350 g
5 × 350 g = 1750 g
2200 g − 1750 g = 450 g
450 g ÷ 3 = 150 g
(3 × 350 g) + (2 × 150 g) = 1050 g + 300 g = 1350 g

....1350.... g

Hints
- If you find this difficult, make up some numbers to fill the gaps, and work out the answer.
- Then, compare the working with your own.
- Adjust the numbers in the question to match.

3 Use the student's working out and answer to complete the question.

12 Michael is the manager of a swimming club.
He interviews some swimmers to find out their favourite swimming stroke.
The table shows this information.

Hint
- The 'Side' column should remain empty in the question.

Stroke	Back	Butterfly	Crawl	Side
Proportion	$\frac{6}{25}$	0.28	$\frac{1}{4}$	

Write the swimming strokes in ....order.... of popularity.
Start with the ....least.... popular. **(3 marks)**

$\frac{6}{25} = 0.24$, $\frac{1}{4} = 0.25$,
0.24 + 0.25 + 0.28 = 0.77
1 − 0.77 = 0.23
0.23, $\frac{6}{25}$, $\frac{1}{4}$, 0.28

side, back, crawl, butterfly

Improve the answer

1 Write an improved answer that would be awarded 2 marks.

10 Work out 3 × (4 + 6 ÷ 2) **(2 marks)**

The student has not applied BIDMAS within the brackets.

Nearly there

3 × (10 ÷ 2) = 3 × 5 = 15
....15....

3 × (4 + 3) = 3 × 7 = 21
....21....

2 Write an improved answer that would be awarded 4 marks.

16 Calvino buys 80 mangoes for £60
He sells 12 boxes of six mangoes at £6.50 per box.
The rest of the mangoes are sold at 95p each.
Work out how much profit he makes. **(4 marks)**

The student has not converted 95p to pounds.

Nearly there

12 × 6.50 = 78
12 × 6 = 72
80 − 72 = 8
8 × 95 = 760
78 + 760 = 838
Profit = £838 − £60 = £778
£....778....

12 × 6.50 = 78
12 × 6 = 72
80 − 72 = 8
8 × 0.95 = 7.60
78 + 7.60 = 85.60
Profit = £85.60 − £60 = £25.60
£....25.60....

3 Write an improved answer that would be awarded 3 marks.

11 In a shop, pencil cases cost £1.75 each.
Taran has £20
He wants to buy as many pencil cases as possible.
How many can he buy and how much change should he receive? **(3 marks)**

Had a go

20 ÷ 1.75 = 11.428
Cost of pencil cases = 12 × 1.75 = £21
Change = £21 − £20 = £1
Taran can buy 12 pencil cases. He should receive £1 change.

If I have time, I read through the question again and make sure my working and answer make sense. This helps me spot silly mistakes!

20 ÷ 1.75 = 11.428
Cost of pencil cases = 11 × 1.75 = £19.25
Change = £20 − £19.25 = £0.75 = 75p
Taran can buy 11 pencil cases. He should receive 75p change.

Find the answer

1 Find the answer that would be awarded 2 marks. Choose **A**, **B** or **C**. Explain your choice.

4 Work out 60% of 120 **(2 marks)**

A: 10% = 120 ÷ 10 = 12; 60% = 6 × 12 = 72

B: 10% = 120 ÷ 100 = 1.2; 60% = 6 × 1.2 = 7.2

C: 10% = 120 ÷ 10 = 12; 40% = 4 × 12; 60% = 100 − 48 = 52

Answer ..A.. would get 2 marks because the student has correctly worked out 10% and then multiplied by 6 to get the correct answer.

2 For each part of the question, find the answer that would be awarded the mark. Choose **A**, **B** or **C**. Explain your choice.

5 Write these calculations as a single power.

(a) $5^4 \times 5^2$ **(1 mark)**

A $5^{4-2} = 5^2$ B $5^{4+2} = 5^6$ C $25^{4+2} = 25^6$

Answer ..B.. would get the mark because the student has correctly added the powers.

(b) $5^9 \div 5^6$ **(1 mark)**

A $5^{9-6} = 5^3$ B $5^{9+6} = 5^{15}$ C $1^{9-6} = 1^3$

Answer ..A.. would get the mark because the student has correctly subtracted the powers.

(c) $(5^4)^3$ **(1 mark)**

A $5^{4-3} = 5^1$ B $5^{4+3} = 5^7$ C $5^{4\times3} = 5^{12}$

Answer ..C.. would get the mark because the student has correctly multiplied the powers.

3 Find the answer that would be awarded the mark. Choose **A**, **B** or **C**. Explain your choice.

3 Work out $\sqrt{64} \times \sqrt[3]{27}$ **(1 mark)**

A 8 × 3 = 24   B 4 × 3 = 12   C 8 × 9 = 72

Answer ..A.. would get the mark because the student has correctly worked out the square root of 64 and the cube root of 27, and multiplied the results.

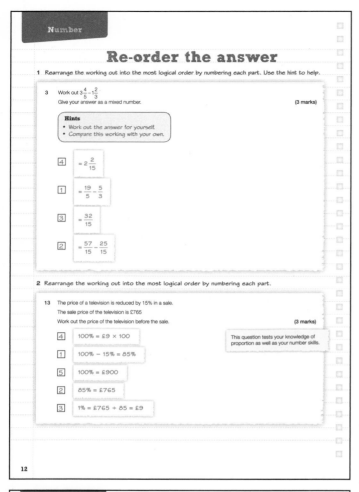

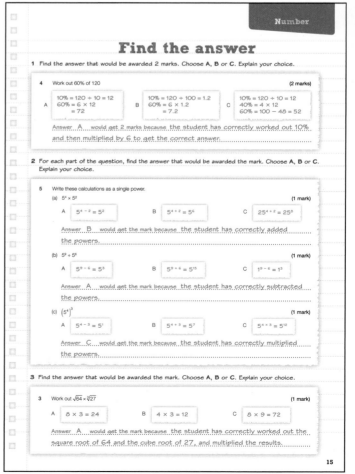

Number

Mark the answer

1 Use the mark scheme to assign a mark to the answer. Explain your decision.

18 Ruth is going to have a party. There will be 60 people at the party.
Ruth wants to buy enough samosas so that each person at the party can have 2 samosas.
There are 7 samosas in each pack. Ruth buys 16 packs of samosas.

Has she bought enough samosas? (3 marks)

Number of samosas needed = 60 × 2 = 120
Number of samosas Ruth buys = 16 × 7 = 112 ....112........

Answer	Notes
No as 112 < 120	P1 process to find the number of samosas needed e.g. 60 × 2 (=120) P1 process to find the number of samosas bought e.g. 16 × 7 (= 112) A1 cao

I would award the answer 2 out of 3 marks because the student has correctly worked out the number of samosas needed and the number of samosas bought. The student does not get the final mark because they have not answered the question.

2 Use the mark scheme to assign marks to the answers. Explain your decisions.

4 (a) Find the highest common factor (HCF) of 32 and 48 (2 marks)

32 = 1 × 32, 2 × 16, 4 × 8
48 = 1 × 48, 2 × 24, 3 × 16, 4 × 12, 6 × 8
Factors of 32: 1, 2, 4, 8, 16, 32
Factors of 48: 1, 2, 3, 4, 6, 8, 12, 16, 24, 48
HCF = 16 ....16........

I make sure I write down all my working because I know I might not get all the marks if I don't – even if my final answer is correct.

Answer	Notes
16	M1 lists the factors of 32 and 48 A1 cao

I would award the answer 2 out of 2 marks because the student has correctly worked out the HCF and shown their working clearly.

(b) Find the lowest common multiple (LCM) of 32 and 48 (2 marks)

Multiples of 32: 32, 64, 96, 128, 160
Multiples of 48: 48, 96 LCM = 96 ....96........

Answer	Notes
96	M1 lists the multiples of 32 and 48 A1 cao

I would award the answer 2 out of 2 marks because the student has correctly worked out the LCM and shown their working clearly.

16

Number

Complete the question

1 Use the student's working out and answer to complete the question.

17 The alarms on Sandra's and Pavel's phones sound together at 7.30 am.
Sandra's alarm then sounds every 8 minutes.
Pavel's alarm then sounds every 11 minutes.
Show that both of their alarms will next sound together at 8.58 am. (3 marks)

Nailed it!

Sandra: 8 16 24 32 40 48 56 64 72 80 88 96
Pavel: 11 22 33 44 55 66 77 88 99

88 minutes = 1 hour 28 minutes
7.30 + 1 h 28 = 8.58

2 Use the student's working out and answer to complete the question.

Hint
- The question uses mixed units of length.

11 Adam has 20 m of rope on a reel.
He cuts 4 pieces of rope off the reel.
The lengths of the pieces are 95 cm, 4.43 m, 10.65 m and 167 cm.
Work out how much rope, in metres, Adam has left on the reel. (3 marks)

Nailed it!

95 + 443 + 1065 + 167 = 1770
2000 − 1770 = 230
Amount of rope on the reel = 2.3 m ....2.3........ m

3 Use the student's working out and answer to complete the question.

20 The diagram shows a large circle and two small circles.
Area of circle B = $\frac{3}{2}\pi$ cm²
The area of circle B is twice the area of circle A.
The area of the large circle is six times the area of circle B.
Work out the shaded area. Leave your answer in terms of π. (3 marks)

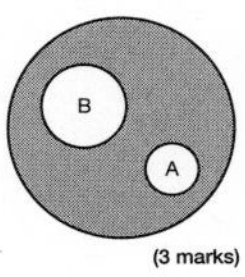

Nailed it!

Area of circle A = $\frac{3}{4}\pi$ cm²
Area of large circle = $\frac{18}{2}\pi = 9\pi$ cm²
Shaded area = $9\pi - \frac{3}{2}\pi - \frac{3}{4}\pi = \frac{36}{4}\pi - \frac{6}{4}\pi - \frac{3}{4}\pi = \frac{27}{4}\pi$ ....$\frac{27}{4}\pi$........ cm²

17

Number

Complete the answer

1 Use the hint below to complete the student's answer so that it would be awarded 3 marks.

9 Washing powder is sold in three sizes: 2 kg, 5 kg and 9 kg.
A 2 kg box of washing powder costs £1.79
A 5 kg box of washing powder costs £4.40
A 9 kg box of washing powder costs £8.10
Which size is the best value for money?
You must show how you get your answer. (3 marks)

Hint
- Work out the cost per kilogram for each size of box.

2 kg box = 1.79 ÷ 2 = £0.895
5 kg box = 4.40 ÷ 5 = £0.88
9 kg box = 8.10 ÷ 9 = £0.90
The 5 kg box is the best value for money.

2 Use the hint below to complete the student's answer so that it would be awarded 3 marks.

6 Leon and Sal both work in restaurants.
Leon gets basic pay of £80 per day.
Sal gets basic pay of £84 per day.
One day, Leon gets a bonus of 30% of his basic pay.
On the same day, Sal gets £15 in tips.
Work out the difference between the total amounts of money that Leon and Sal each get that day. (3 marks)

Hint
- First, work out the total amounts of money that Leon and Sal each get that day.

10% of £80 = £8
30% of £80 = 3 × 8 = £24
Leon = £80 + £24 = £104
Sal = £84 + £15 = £99
Difference = £104 − £99 = £5 £........5........

3 Use the hints below to complete the student's answer so that it would be awarded 3 marks.

3 Express 180 as a product of its prime factors. (3 marks)

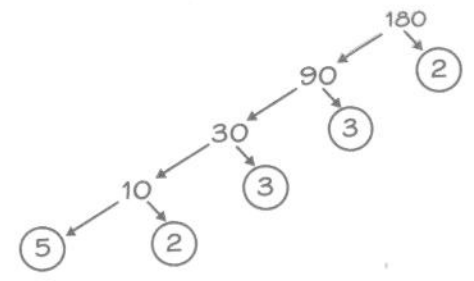

Hints
- Use the factor tree to help you divide 180 until you reach its prime factors.
- Remember to use indices in your answer.
- It doesn't matter what your factor tree looks like, as long as you have the correct final answer.

180 = 2 × 3 × 3 × 2 × 5 ....$180 = 2^2 \times 3^2 \times 5$........

18

Algebra

Improve the answer

1 For each part of the question, write an improved answer that would be awarded full marks.

20 Here is a grid showing the points A and B.

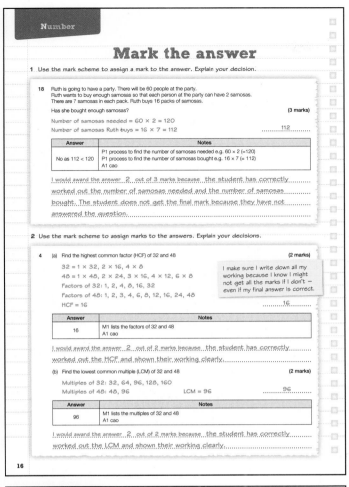

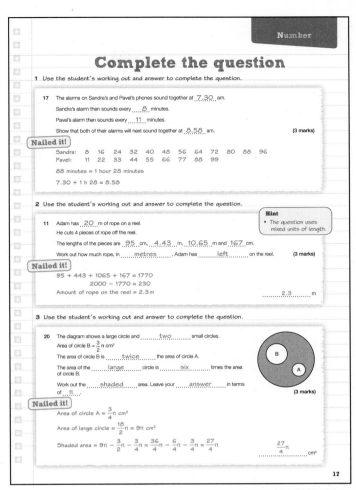

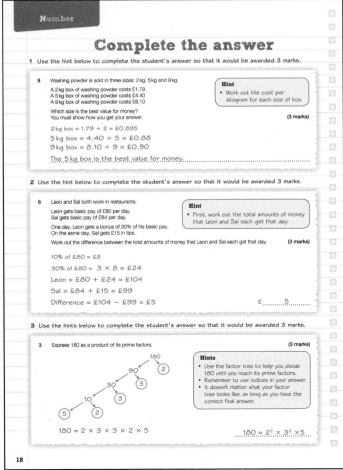

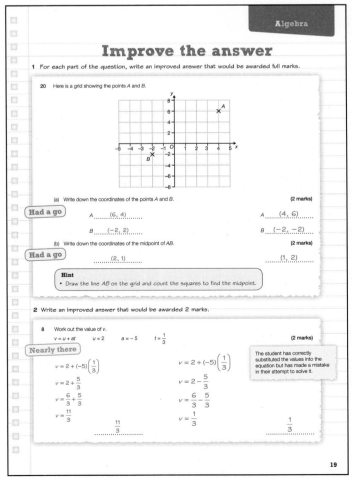

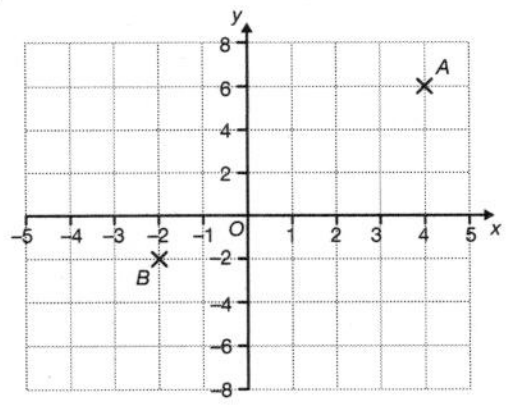

(a) Write down the coordinates of the points A and B. (2 marks)

Had a go

A ....(6, 4)........ A ....(4, 6)........
B ....(−2, 2)........ B ....(−2, −2)........

(b) Write down the coordinates of the midpoint of AB. (2 marks)

Had a go

........(2, 1)........ ....(1, 2)........

Hint
- Draw the line AB on the grid and count the squares to find the midpoint.

2 Write an improved answer that would be awarded 2 marks.

8 Work out the value of v.
$v = u + at$ $u = 2$ $a = -5$ $t = \frac{1}{3}$ (2 marks)

Nearly there

The student has correctly substituted the values into the equation but has made a mistake in their attempt to solve it.

$v = 2 + (-5)\left(\frac{1}{3}\right)$ | $v = 2 + (-5)\left(\frac{1}{3}\right)$
$v = 2 + \frac{5}{3}$ | $v = 2 - \frac{5}{3}$
$v = \frac{6}{3} + \frac{5}{3}$ | $v = \frac{6}{3} - \frac{5}{3}$
$v = \frac{11}{3}$ | $v = \frac{1}{3}$

........$\frac{11}{3}$........ ....$\frac{1}{3}$........

19

Answers

Find the answer

1 For each part of the question, find the answer that would be awarded full marks. Choose A, B or C. Explain your choice.

(a) Simplify $5x + 4y + 3x - 9y$ **(2 marks)**

A $8x - 5y$ B $2x - 13y$ C $8x + 5y$

Answer A would get 2 marks because the student has correctly collected the like terms, taking the signs into consideration.

(b) Factorise $y^2 - 4y$ **(1 mark)**

A $y(y + 4)$ B $y(y - 4)$ C $4y(y - 1)$

Answer B would get the mark because the student has correctly found the common factor and then factorised the expression correctly.

(c) Expand $y(y^3 + 2y)$ **(2 marks)**

A $y^4 + 2y$ B $y^3 + 2y^2$ C $y^4 + 2y^2$

Answer C would get 2 marks because the student has correctly used the index laws and multiplied both terms in the bracket correctly.

2 Find the answer that would be awarded 3 marks. Choose A, B or C. Explain your choice.

4 Here are three graphs.

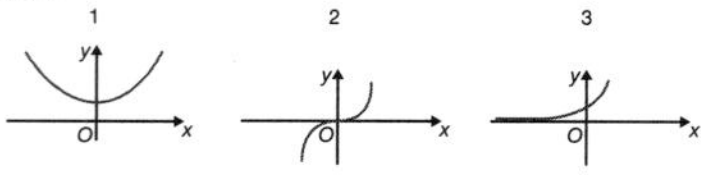

Here are four equations of graphs.

$y = 3^x$ $y = x^3$ $y = x^2 + 3$ $y = \frac{2}{x}$

Match each graph to the correct equation. **(3 marks)**

A: 1 is $y = x^2 + 3$, 2 is $y = x^3$, 3 is $y = 3^x$

B: 1 is $y = x^3$, 2 is $y = x^2 + 3$, 3 is $y = 3^x$

C: 1 is $y = x^3$, 2 is $y = x^2 + 3$, 3 is $y = \frac{2}{x}$

Answer A would get 3 marks because the student has correctly identified the shape of each graph.

Mark the answer

1 Use the mark scheme to assign a mark to the answer. Explain your decision.

13 Solve the simultaneous equations

① $3x + 10y = 7$

② $x - 4y = 6$ **(3 marks)**

③: ② × 3 $3x - 12y = 18$ Substitute $3x + 10(-0.5) = 7$

③ − ① $22y = -11$ $3x = 7 - 5$

$y = -0.5$ $x = \frac{2}{3}$

$x = \frac{2}{3}, y = -\frac{1}{2}$

Answer	Notes
$x = 4, y = -0.5$	M1 for a correct method to eliminate one variable M1 for a correct method to find second variable A1 for $x = 4, y = -0.5$

I would award the answer 2 out of 3 marks because the student has eliminated the first variable and correctly substituted $y = -0.5$ into one of the equations. However, they have made a mistake rearranging the equation to find x, so lose the final mark.

2 Use the mark scheme to assign a mark to the answer. Explain your decision.

14 Albert has x counters. Ben has twice as many counters as Albert. Chris has 7 more counters than Albert. They have a total of 43 counters.

Work out how many counters Albert, Ben and Chris each have. **(5 marks)**

$x + 2x + x + 7 = 4x + 7 = 43$

$4x = 36$

$x = 9$

$2x = 2 \times 9 = 18$

$x + 7 = 9 + 7 = 16$

Albert has 9 counters, Ben has 18 and Chris has 16

Answer	Notes
9, 18 and 16	P1 process to set up an expression for the total number of counters e.g. $x + 2x + x + 7$ or $4x + 7$ P1 process to set up an equation for the counters e.g. $x + 2x + x + 7 = 43$ or $4x + 7 = 43$ P1 process to solve the equation e.g. $x = (43 - 7) \div 4$ (= 9) P1 process to work out the numbers of counters e.g. 2×9 and $9 + 7$ A1 for 9, 18 and 16

I would award the answer 5 out of 5 marks because the student has correctly written down and solved an equation, then found how many counters each person has.

Re-order the answer

1 Rearrange the working out into the most logical order by numbering each part. Use the hints to help.

11 Solve $\frac{7^6 \times 7^x}{7^2} = 7^5$ **(4 marks)**

[3] $6 + x - 2 = 5$

[1] $\frac{7^{6+x}}{7^2} = 7^5$

[5] $x = 1$

[2] $7^{6+x-2} = 7^5$

[4] $x = 5 + 2 - 6$

Hints
- Deal with the powers in the numerator first.
- Then, look at the denominator.

2 Rearrange the working out into the most logical order by numbering each part. Use the hint to help.

20 The diagram shows a triangle.

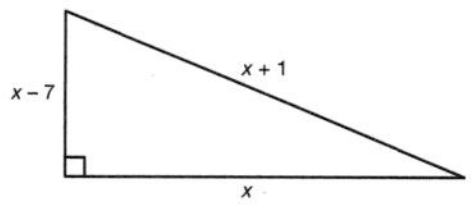

In the diagram, all the measurements are in centimetres.

The perimeter of the triangle is 30 cm.
The area of the triangle is A cm².

Work out the value of A. **(4 marks)**

Hint
- First, set up an equation and solve it to find the value of x.

[3] $x = 12$

[5] $= 30$

[2] $3x = 36$

[1] $x + x - 7 + x + 1 = 30$

[4] $0.5 \times 12 \times 5$

Complete the question

1 Use the student's working out and answer to complete the question.

7 Expand and simplify $(x - 4)(x + 6)$ **(2 marks)**

Nailed it!

$x^2 + 6x - 4x - 24 = x^2 + 2x - 24$

$x^2 + 2x - 24$

Hint
- You need to provide an expression as two brackets. It doesn't matter which way round you write them into the question; the answer will still be the same.

2 Use the student's answer to complete the question.

10 Write down the inequality represented on the number line. **(1 mark)**

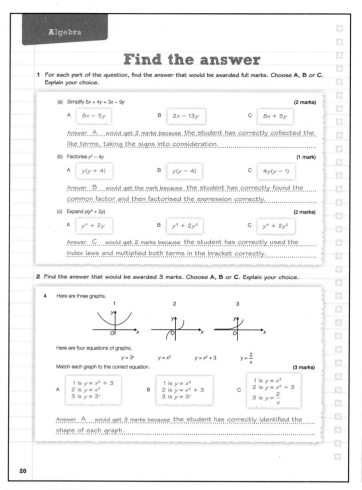

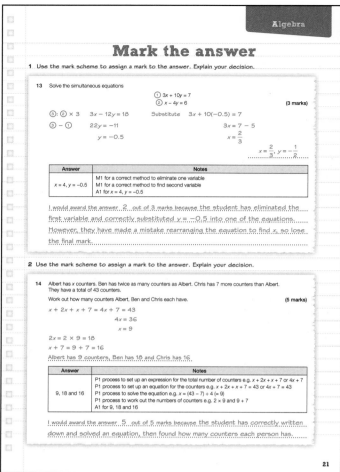

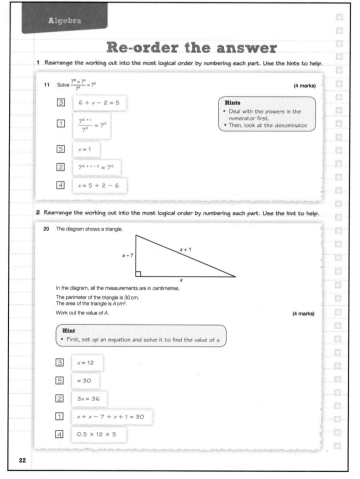

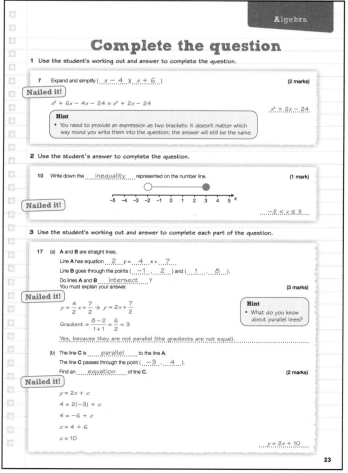

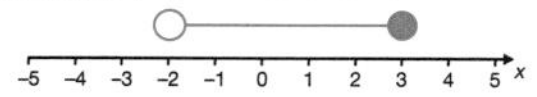

Nailed it!

$-2 < x \leq 3$

3 Use the student's working out and answer to complete each part of the question.

17 (a) **A** and **B** are straight lines.

Line **A** has equation $2y = 4x + 7$.

Line **B** goes through the points (−1, 2) and (1, 8).

Do lines **A** and **B** intersect?

You must explain your answer. **(3 marks)**

Nailed it!

$y = \frac{4}{2}x + \frac{7}{2} \rightarrow y = 2x + \frac{7}{2}$

Gradient $= \frac{8 - 2}{1 + 1} = \frac{6}{2} = 3$

Yes, because they are not parallel (the gradients are not equal).

Hint
- What do you know about parallel lines?

(b) The line **C** is parallel to the line **A**.

The line **C** passes through the point (−3, 4).

Find an equation of line **C**. **(2 marks)**

Nailed it!

$y = 2x + c$

$4 = 2(-3) + c$

$4 = -6 + c$

$c = 4 + 6$

$c = 10$

$y = 2x + 10$

Complete the answer

1 For each part of the question, complete the student's answer so that it would be awarded full marks.

9 (a) Complete the table of values for $y = 3x + 4$ **(2 marks)**

x	−2	−1	0	1	2	3
y	−2	1	4	7	10	13

$y = 3x + 4 = 3(-2) + 4 = -6 + 4 = -2$

$y = 3x + 4 = 3(-1) + 4 = -3 + 4 = 1$

$y = 3x + 4 = 3(1) + 4 = 3 + 4 = 7$

$y = 3x + 4 = 3(2) + 4 = 6 + 4 = 10$

Hint
- Use the same method to work out the remaining missing values.

(b) On the grid, draw the graph of $y = 3x + 4$ **(2 marks)**

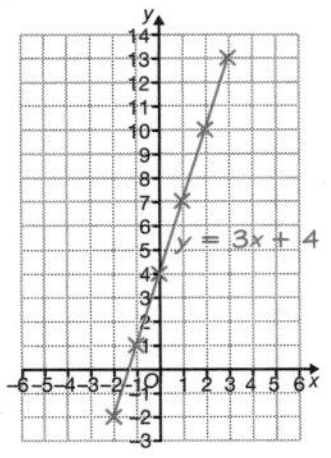

When I'm drawing a straight-line graph, I know I've made a mistake if the points don't all lie on the line.

2 For each part of the question, complete the student's answer so that it would be awarded full marks.

4 Here are the first four terms of an arithmetic sequence.

4 9 14 19

(a) Write down the next two terms of the sequence. **(1 mark)**

4 → 9 → 14 → 19 (+5, +5, +5)

$19 + 5 = 24$

$24 + 5 = 29$

Hint
- Use the term-to-term rule to generate the next two terms.

24, 29

(b) Write an expression, in terms of n, for the nth term of the sequence. **(2 marks)**

$5n$

term $0 = 4 - 5 = -1$

Hint
- $5n$ is part of the expression for the nth term. Use the term-to-term rule to find term 0 and complete the expression.

$5n - 1$

Improve the answer

1 Write an improved answer that would be awarded 3 marks.

4 Solve $x^2 - 5x - 24 = 0$ **(3 marks)**

Nearly there

$(+8) \times (-3) = -24$ and $(+8) + (-3) = 5$

$(x + 8)(x - 3) = 0$

$(x + 8) = 0$ or $(x - 3) = 0$

$x = -8$ or $x = 3$

$x = -8$ or $x = 3$

The student has attempted to factorise but has made an error with the signs.

$(-8) \times (+3) = -24$ and $(-8) + (+3) = -5$

$(x - 8)(x + 3) = 0$

$(x - 8) = 0$ or $(x + 3) = 0$

$x = 8$ or $x = -3$

$x = 8$ or $x = -3$

2 Write an improved answer that would be awarded 4 marks.

8 ABC is a triangle.

Angle ABC = angle ACB
Length of side $AB = (3x + 8)$ cm
Length of side $AC = (20 - x)$ cm
Length of side $BC = (3x)$ cm

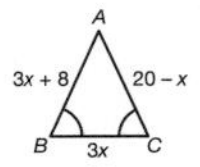

Work out the perimeter, in cm, of the triangle. **(4 marks)**

Nearly there

$3x + 8 = 20 - x$

$3x + x = 20 + 8$

$4x = 28$

$x = 7$

Perimeter $= 3(7) + 8 + 20 - 7 + 3(7)$

$= 21 + 8 + 20 - 7 + 21$

$= 63$

63 cm

The student has correctly identified that the triangle is isosceles and set up an equation. However, they have made an error when attempting to solve it.

$3x + 8 = 20 - x$

$3x + x = 20 - 8$

$4x = 12$

$x = 3$

Perimeter $= 3(3) + 8 + 20 - 3 + 3(3)$

$= 9 + 8 + 20 - 3 + 9$

$= 43$

43 cm

Find the answer

1 For each part of the question, find the answer that would be awarded full marks. Choose **A**, **B** or **C**. Explain your choice.

7 (a) Simplify $3(2x - 1) - 2(2x - 3)$ **(2 marks)**

A: $6x - 3 - 4x + 6 = 2x + 3$

B: $6x - 3 - 4x - 6 = 2x - 9$

C: $6x - 3 - 4x + 6 = 2x - 3$

Answer A would get 2 marks because the student has correctly multiplied out the brackets and then collected the like terms, taking the signs into consideration.

(b) Simplify $4x^4y^5 \times 3x^2y^3$ **(2 marks)**

A: $12 \times x^8 \times y^{15} = 12x^8y^{15}$

B: $12 \times x^6 \times y^8 = 12x^6y^8$

C: $7 \times x^6 \times y^8 = 7x^6y^8$

Answer B would get 2 marks because the student has correctly multiplied the coefficients and added the powers to obtain the answer.

2 Find the answer that would be awarded 4 marks. Choose **A**, **B** or **C**. Explain your choice.

20 By drawing two suitable straight lines on a coordinate grid, solve the simultaneous equations.

$y = x + 1$
$x + y = 7$

(4 marks)

A

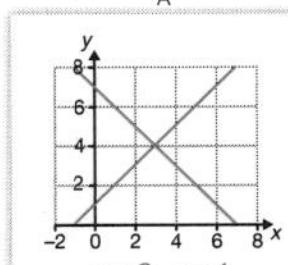

$x = 3, y = 4$

B

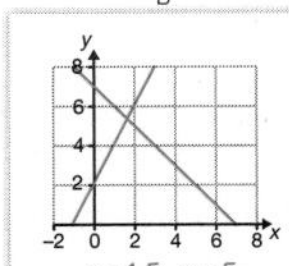

$x = 1.5, y = 5$

C

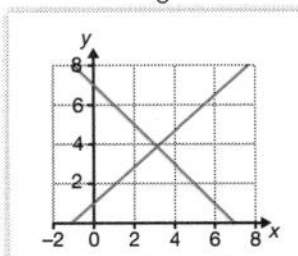

$x = 4, y = 3$

Answer A would get 4 marks because the student has correctly drawn the two straight lines and interpreted the coordinates of the point of intersection correctly.

Mark the answer

1 Use the mark scheme to assign a mark to the answer. Explain your decision.

3 The nth term of a sequence is $2n^2 - 15$

Work out the 4th term of this sequence. **(1 mark)**

$2 \times 4^2 - 15 = 8^2 - 15 = 64 - 15 = 49$

49

Answer	Notes
17	B1 cao

I would award the answer 0 out of 1 mark because the student has incorrectly calculated the term so their final answer is wrong.

2 Use the mark scheme to assign a mark to the answer. Explain your decision.

8 The diagram shows a patio in the shape of a trapezium.

All the measurements are in metres.
The area of the patio is 220 m².

Work out the value of x. **(5 marks)**

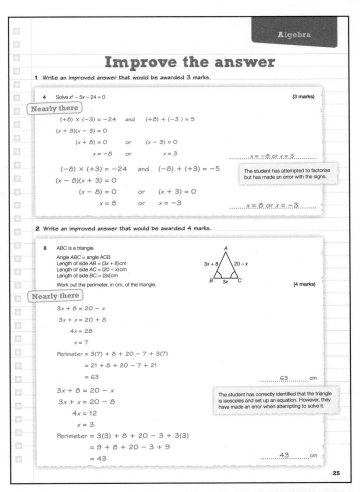

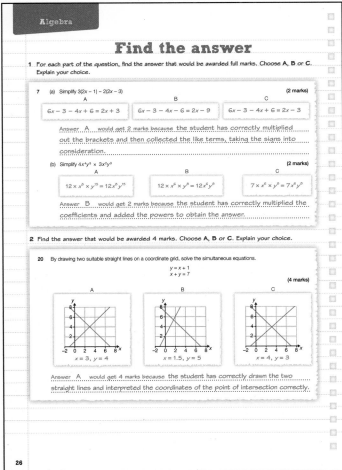

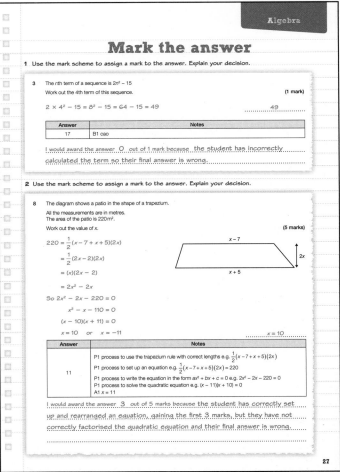

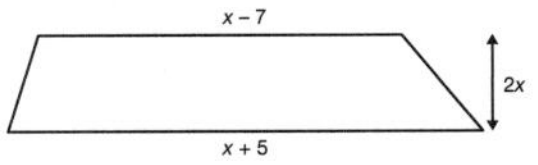

$220 = \frac{1}{2}(x - 7 + x + 5)(2x)$

$= \frac{1}{2}(2x - 2)(2x)$

$= (x)(2x - 2)$

$= 2x^2 - 2x$

So $2x^2 - 2x - 220 = 0$

$x^2 - x - 110 = 0$

$(x - 10)(x + 11) = 0$

$x = 10$ or $x = -11$

$x = 10$

Answer	Notes
11	P1 process to use the trapezium rule with correct lengths e.g. $\frac{1}{2}(x - 7 + x + 5)(2x)$ P1 process to set up an equation e.g. $\frac{1}{2}(x - 7 + x + 5)(2x) = 220$ P1 process to write the equation in the form $ax^2 + bx + c = 0$ e.g. $2x^2 - 2x - 220 = 0$ P1 process to solve the quadratic equation e.g. $(x - 11)(x + 10) = 0$ A1 $x = 11$

I would award the answer 3 out of 5 marks because the student has correctly set up and rearranged an equation, gaining the first 3 marks, but they have not correctly factorised the quadratic equation and their final answer is wrong.

Find the answer

1 For each part of the question, find the answer that would be awarded full marks. Choose **A**, **B** or **C**. Explain your choice.

15 (a) Show that $(x-2)^2 = x^2 - 4x + 4$ **(2 marks)**

A
$(x-2)^2 = (x-2)(x-2)$
$= x^2 - 2x - 2x + 4$
$= x^2 - 4x + 4$

B
$(x-2)^2 = (x-2)(x+2)$
$= x^2 - 2x + 2x - 4$
$= x^2 - 4x + 4$

C
$(x-2)^2 = (x-2)(x-2)$
$= x^2 + 2x + 2x + 4$
$= x^2 - 4x + 4$

Answer A would get 2 marks because the student has correctly multiplied out the brackets. When like terms are collected, they give $x^2 - 4x + 4$

(b) Using your answer from part (a), show that $(x+2)^2 + (x-2)^2 = 2(x^2 + 4)$. **(2 marks)**

A
$(x+2)^2 = (x+2)(x+2)$
$= x^2 + 2x + 2x + 4$
$= x^2 + 4x + 4$
$x^2 + 4x + 4 + x^2 - 4x + 4$
$= 2x^2 + 8$

B
$(x+2)^2 = (x+2)(x+2)$
$= x^2 + 2x + 2x + 4$
$= x^2 + 4x + 4$
$x^2 + 4x + 4 + x^2 - 4x + 4$
$= 2x^2 + 8$
$= 2(x^2 + 4)$

C
$(x+2)^2 = (x+2)(x+2)$
$= x^2 + 2x + 2x + 4$
$= x^2 + 4x + 4$
$x^2 + 4x + 4 + x^2 - 4x + 4$
$= 2x^2 + 8x$
$= 2(x^2 + 4x)$

Answer B would get 2 marks because the student has correctly multiplied out the brackets and collected like terms, taking the signs into consideration. They have then checked that their final answer matches the expression given in the question.

2 Find the answer that would be awarded the mark. Choose **A**, **B** or **C**. Explain your choice.

8 x is greater than −4 and less than 7
Write the information as a single inequality. **(1 mark)**

A $x > -4$ and $x < 7$ B $-4 > x > 7$ C $-4 < x < 7$

Answer C would get the mark because the student has written the answer as a single inequality, with the correct inequality signs.

3 Find the answer that would be awarded the mark. Choose **A**, **B** or **C**. Explain your choice.

10 Rearrange $x = y + 7$ to make y the subject. **(1 mark)**

A $y = x + 7$ B $y = x - 7$ C $x + y = 7$

Answer B would get the mark because the student has rearranged the equation correctly.

Complete the answer

1 Use the hint below to complete the student's answer so that it would be awarded 3 marks.

4 List the integer values that satisfy the inequality $-1 < 2x - 1 \leqslant 10$ **(3 marks)**

$-1 < 2x - 1$
$-1 + 1 < 2x$
$0 < 2x$
$x > 0$

$2x - 1 \leqslant 10$
$2x \leqslant 10 + 1$
$2x \leqslant 11$
$x \leqslant 5.5$

Integer values are 1, 2, 3, 4, 5

Hint
- Treat $-1 < 2x - 1 \leqslant 10$ as two separate inequalities. Solve them both for x.

2 Use the hints below to complete the student's answer so that it would be awarded 2 marks.

11 The table shows the values for a straight line.

x	−1	0	1	2	3
y	−8	−5	−2	1	4

Work out the equation of the line. **(2 marks)**

Gradient goes up 3 and across 1
$m = 3$
The intercept on the y-axis is −5
$y = 3x - 5$

Hints
- The gradient, m, is $\frac{\text{change in } y}{\text{change in } x}$
- The y-intercept, c, is the y-value when $x = 0$
- Write your answer in the form $y = mx + c$.

3 Use the hint below to complete the student's answer so that it would be awarded 3 marks.

11 $\frac{x}{3} = 4$ and $\frac{20}{y} = 4$
Work out xy. **(3 marks)**

$x = 4 \times 3$
$= 12$
$y = \frac{20}{4}$
$y = 5$
$xy = 12 \times 5$
$xy = 60$

60

Hint
- First, work out the values of x and y.

4 Use the hint below to complete the student's answer so that it would be awarded 3 marks.

17 $P = 3n + m$.
n is an integer and m is one more than n.
Show that P is always an odd number. **(3 marks)**

$m = n + 1$
$P = 3n + n + 1$
$P = 4n + 1$
$4n$ is an even number. Therefore $4n + 1$ is always an odd number.

Hint
- Write P in terms of n only.

Improve the answer

1 Write an improved answer that would be awarded 2 marks.

13 Factorise fully $6x^4y + 24x^3y^4$ **(2 marks)**

Nearly there

$6x^3y(x + 3y^3)$ $6x^3y(x + 4y^3)$

The student has made a mistake with one of the factors.

2 Write an improved answer that would be awarded 3 marks.

8 $3x + 4 + ax + b = 2(5x + 3)$
Given that a and b are integers, work out the value of a and the value of b. **(3 marks)**

Nearly there

$ax + b = 2(5x + 3) - 3x + 4$
$= 10x + 6 - 3x + 4$
$= 7x + 10$
$a =$ 7
$b =$ 10

$ax + b = 2(5x + 3) - (3x + 4)$
$= 10x + 6 - 3x - 4$
$= 7x + 2$
$a =$ 7
$b =$ 2

The student has identified the need to subtract $3x + 4$ from $2(5x + 3)$ but has made a mistake in their working.

3 Write an improved answer that would be awarded 3 marks.

7 Solve $\frac{12 - 2x}{4} = 6$ **(3 marks)**

Nearly there

$12 - 2x = 24$
$-2x = 24 + 12$
$-2x = 36$
$x = \frac{36}{-2}$
$x = -18$
−18

$12 - 2x = 24$
$-2x = 24 - 12$
$-2x = 12$
$x = \frac{12}{-2}$
$x = -6$
−6

The student has correctly multiplied out the denominator, but has then made a mistake in their working.

Find the answer

1 Find the answer that would be awarded the mark. Choose **A**, **B** or **C**. Explain your choice.

4 Simplify $x^6 \div x^2$ **(1 mark)**

A $x^{6+2} = x^8$ B $x^{6 \div 2} = x^3$ C $x^{6-2} = x^4$

Answer C would get the mark because the student has correctly subtracted the powers.

2 Find the answer that would be awarded 2 marks. Choose **A**, **B** or **C**. Explain your choice.

10 Factorise $3x^2 - 48$ **(2 marks)**

A $3(x^2 - 16) = 3(x - 4)(x - 4)$ B $3(x^2 - 16)$ C $3(x^2 - 16) = 3(x - 4)(x + 4)$

Answer C would get 2 marks because the student has factorised the quadratic and then recognised $3(x^2 - 16)$ as the difference of two squares.

3 Find the answer that would be awarded 2 marks. Choose **A**, **B** or **C**. Explain your choice.

5 Solve $6x + 4 \geqslant x + 24$ **(2 marks)**

A
$6x + x \geqslant 24 + 4$
$7x \geqslant 28$
$x \geqslant 4$

B
$6x - x \geqslant 24 - 4$
$5x \geqslant 20$
$x \geqslant 4$

C
$6x - x \geqslant 24 - 4$
$4x \geqslant 14$
$x \geqslant 3.5$

Answer B would get 2 marks because the student has correctly rearranged the inequality to find x.

4 Find the answer that would be awarded 2 marks. Choose **A**, **B** or **C**. Explain your choice.

7 A shop sells boxes of pencils in two sizes, small and large.
There are 5 pencils in each small box.
There are 7 pencils in each large box.
Xian buys x small boxes of pencils and y large boxes of pencils.
Write down an expression, in terms of x and y, for the total number of pencils Xian buys. **(2 marks)**

A $5x + 7y$ B $7x + 5y$ C $35xy$

Answer A would get 2 marks because the student has written down the correct expression.

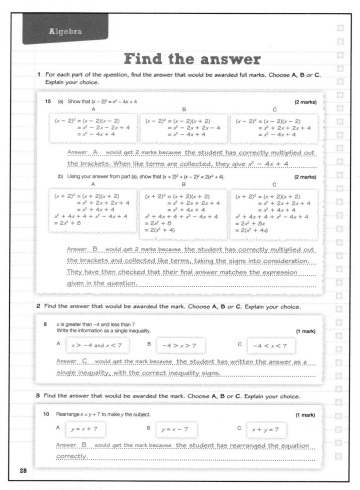

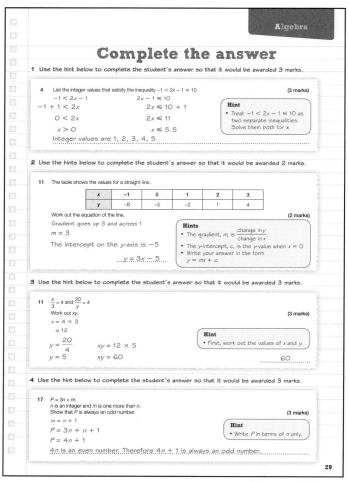

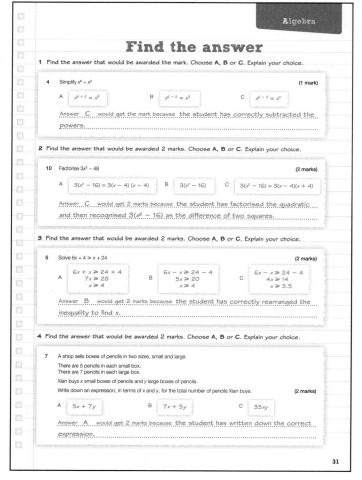

Complete the answer

1 Complete parts (b), (c) and (d) of the student's answer so that they would be awarded full marks.

15 (a) Complete the table of values for $y = x^2 - 5x + 3$ (2 marks)

Nailed it!

x	−1	0	1	2	3	4	5
y	9	3	−1	−3	−3	−1	3

(b) On the grid, draw the graph of $y = x^2 - 5x + 3$ for all values of x from −1 to 5 (2 marks)

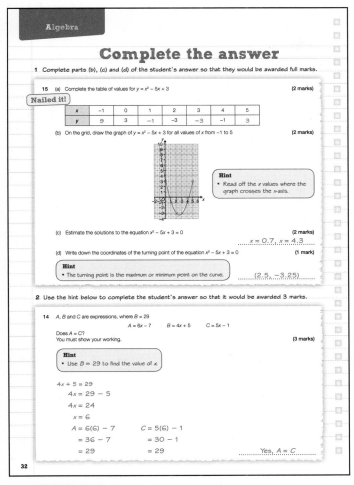

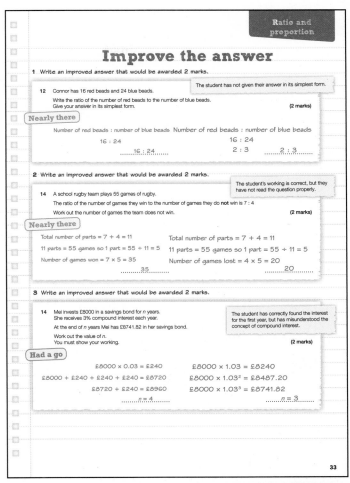

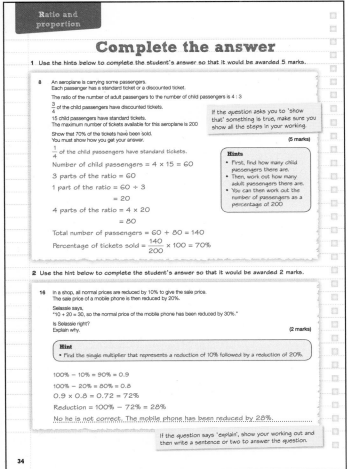

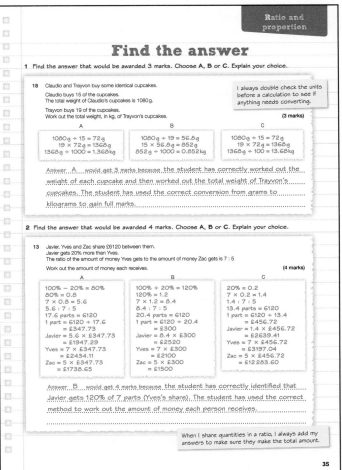

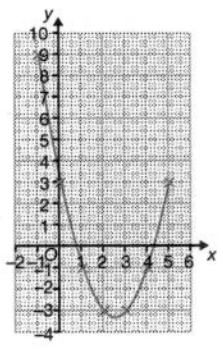

Hint
- Read off the x values where the graph crosses the x-axis.

(c) Estimate the solutions to the equation $x^2 - 5x + 3 = 0$ (2 marks)

$x = 0.7$, $x = 4.3$

(d) Write down the coordinates of the turning point of the equation $x^2 - 5x + 3 = 0$ (1 mark)

Hint
- The turning point is the maximum or minimum point on the curve.

(2.5, −3.25)

2 Use the hint below to complete the student's answer so that it would be awarded 3 marks.

14 A, B and C are expressions, where $B = 29$

$A = 6x - 7$ $B = 4x + 5$ $C = 5x - 1$

Does $A = C$?
You must show your working. (3 marks)

Hint
- Use $B = 29$ to find the value of x.

$4x + 5 = 29$
$4x = 29 - 5$
$4x = 24$
$x = 6$

$A = 6(6) - 7 = 36 - 7 = 29$ $C = 5(6) - 1 = 30 - 1 = 29$

Yes, $A = C$

Improve the answer

1 Write an improved answer that would be awarded 2 marks.

The student has not given their answer in its simplest form.

12 Connor has 16 red beads and 24 blue beads.
Write the ratio of the number of red beads to the number of blue beads.
Give your answer in its simplest form. (2 marks)

Nearly there

Number of red beads : number of blue beads
16 : 24
16 : 24

Number of red beads : number of blue beads
16 : 24
2 : 3
2 : 3

2 Write an improved answer that would be awarded 2 marks.

The student's working is correct, but they have not read the question properly.

14 A school rugby team plays 55 games of rugby.
The ratio of the number of games they win to the number of games they do **not** win is 7 : 4
Work out the number of games the team does not win. (2 marks)

Nearly there

Total number of parts = 7 + 4 = 11
11 parts = 55 games so 1 part = 55 ÷ 11 = 5
Number of games won = 7 × 5 = 35
35

Total number of parts = 7 + 4 = 11
11 parts = 55 games so 1 part = 55 ÷ 11 = 5
Number of games lost = 4 × 5 = 20
20

3 Write an improved answer that would be awarded 2 marks.

14 Mei invests £8000 in a savings bond for n years.
She receives 3% compound interest each year.
At the end of n years Mei has £8741.82 in her savings bond.
Work out the value of n.
You must show your working. (2 marks)

The student has correctly found the interest for the first year, but has misunderstood the concept of compound interest.

Had a go

£8000 × 0.03 = £240
£8000 + £240 + £240 + £240 = £8720
£8720 + £240 = £8960
$n = 4$

£8000 × 1.03 = £8240
£8000 × 1.03^2 = £8487.20
£8000 × 1.03^3 = £8741.82
$n = 3$

Complete the answer

1 Use the hints below to complete the student's answer so that it would be awarded 5 marks.

8 An aeroplane is carrying some passengers.
Each passenger has a standard ticket or a discounted ticket.
The ratio of the number of adult passengers to the number of child passengers is 4 : 3
$\frac{3}{4}$ of the child passengers have discounted tickets.
15 child passengers have standard tickets.
The maximum number of tickets available for this aeroplane is 200
Show that 70% of the tickets have been sold.
You must show how you get your answer. (5 marks)

If the question asks you to 'show that' something is true, make sure you show all the steps in your working.

$\frac{1}{4}$ of the child passengers have standard tickets.
Number of child passengers = 4 × 15 = 60
3 parts of the ratio = 60
1 part of the ratio = 60 ÷ 3
= 20
4 parts of the ratio = 4 × 20
= 80
Total number of passengers = 60 + 80 = 140
Percentage of tickets sold = $\frac{140}{200}$ × 100 = 70%

Hints
- First, find how many child passengers there are.
- Then, work out how many adult passengers there are.
- You can then work out the number of passengers as a percentage of 200

2 Use the hint below to complete the student's answer so that it would be awarded 2 marks.

16 In a shop, all normal prices are reduced by 10% to give the sale price.
The sale price of a mobile phone is then reduced by 20%.
Selassie says,
"10 + 20 = 30, so the normal price of the mobile phone has been reduced by 30%."
Is Selassie right?
Explain why. (2 marks)

Hint
- Find the single multiplier that represents a reduction of 10% followed by a reduction of 20%.

100% − 10% = 90% = 0.9
100% − 20% = 80% = 0.8
0.9 × 0.8 = 0.72 = 72%
Reduction = 100% − 72% = 28%
No he is not correct. The mobile phone has been reduced by 28%.

If the question says 'explain', show your working out and then write a sentence or two to answer the question.

Find the answer

1 Find the answer that would be awarded 3 marks. Choose A, B or C. Explain your choice.

18 Claudio and Trayvon buy some identical cupcakes.
Claudio buys 15 of the cupcakes.
The total weight of Claudio's cupcakes is 1080 g.
Trayvon buys 19 of the cupcakes.
Work out the total weight, in kg, of Trayvon's cupcakes. (3 marks)

I always double check the units before a calculation to see if anything needs converting.

A	B	C
1080g ÷ 15 = 72g 19 × 72g = 1368g 1368g ÷ 1000 = 1.368kg	1080g ÷ 19 = 56.8g 15 × 56.8g = 852g 852g ÷ 1000 = 0.852kg	1080g ÷ 15 = 72g 19 × 72g = 1368g 1368g ÷ 100 = 13.68kg

Answer A would get 3 marks because the student has correctly worked out the weight of each cupcake and then worked out the total weight of Trayvon's cupcakes. The student has used the correct conversion from grams to kilograms to gain full marks.

2 Find the answer that would be awarded 4 marks. Choose A, B or C. Explain your choice.

13 Javier, Yves and Zac share £6120 between them.
Javier gets 20% more than Yves.
The ratio of the amount of money Yves gets to the amount of money Zac gets is 7 : 5
Work out the amount of money each receives. (4 marks)

A	B	C
100% − 20% = 80% 80% = 0.8 7 × 0.8 = 5.6 5.6 : 7 : 5 17.6 parts = 6120 1 part = 6120 ÷ 17.6 = £347.73 Javier = 5.6 × £347.73 = £1947.29 Yves = 7 × £347.73 = £2434.11 Zac = 5 × £347.73 = £1738.65	100% + 20% = 120% 120% = 1.2 7 × 1.2 = 8.4 8.4 : 7 : 5 20.4 parts = 6120 1 part = 6120 ÷ 20.4 = £300 Javier = 8.4 × £300 = £2520 Yves = 7 × £300 = £2100 Zac = 5 × £300 = £1500	20% = 0.2 7 × 0.2 = 1.4 1.4 : 7 : 5 13.4 parts = 6120 1 part = 6120 ÷ 13.4 = £456.72 Javier = 1.4 × £456.72 = £2639.41 Yves = 7 × £456.72 = £3197.04 Zac = 5 × £456.72 = £12 283.60

Answer B would get 4 marks because the student has correctly identified that Javier gets 120% of 7 parts (Yves's share). The student has used the correct method to work out the amount of money each person receives.

When I share quantities in a ratio, I always add my answers to make sure they make the total amount.

Ratio and proportion

Mark the answer

1 Use the mark scheme to assign a mark to the answer. Explain your decision.

20 Carlton wants to invest £4500 in a bank for 2 years.

Carlton wants to have as much money as possible at the end of 2 years.

Which bank should he invest his £4500 in?

Bank A	Bank B
Compound interest	Compound interest
4% for year 1	5% for year 1
3.5% for year 2	2.5% for year 2

(4 marks)

£4500 × 1.04 × 1.035 = £4843.80
£4500 × 1.05 × 1.025 = £4843.13

Answer	Notes
Bank A	P1 process to find the interest for Bank A or Bank B for Year 1 e.g. 4500 × 1.04 (= 4680) or 4500 × 1.05 (= 4725) P1 process to find the interest for Bank A or Bank B for Year 2 e.g. 4500 × 1.04 × 1.035 (= 4843.80) or 4500 × 1.05 × 1.025 (= 4843.13) P1 complete process to find the interest for both banks for Year 2 A1 cao

I would award the answer 3 out of 4 marks because the student has worked out the interest for the two years for both banks, gaining the first 3 marks. The student does not get the final mark because they have not stated which bank Carlton should choose.

2 Use the mark scheme to assign a mark to the answer. Explain your decision.

20 Anna has £300, Ben has £140 and Khalil has £100

Anna gives some money to Ben and Khalil. The ratio of the amount of money Anna, Ben and Khalil have now is 4 : 3 : 2

How much money did Ben and Khalil each receive from Anna? (4 marks)

4 + 3 + 2 = 9 and £300 + £140 + £100 = £540

Ben = $\frac{3}{9} \times 540 = 180$, Khalil = $\frac{2}{9} \times 540 = 120$

Ben = £180 + £140 = £320 and Khalil = £120 + £100 = £220

Ben £320, Khalil £220

Answer	Notes
Ben £40 and Khalil £20	P1 process to work out the amount of money for Ben or Khalil e.g. $\frac{3}{9} \times 540 (= 180)$ or $\frac{2}{9} \times 540 (= 120)$ P1 complete process to work out the amount of money for Ben and Khalil P1 process to work out the amount of money given to Ben or Khalil e.g. "180" – 140 (= 40) or "120" – 100 (= 20) A1 for 40 and 20

I would award the answer 2 out of 4 marks because the student has correctly worked out the amount of money each person has according to the ratio, gaining the first 2 marks. The student then adds the amounts found to the original amounts, instead of subtracting, so loses the last 2 marks.

Ratio and proportion

Re-order the answer

1 Rearrange the working out into the most logical order by numbering each part. Use the hints to help.

21 Rectangle *ABCD* is similar to rectangle *DAXY*.

DC = 15 cm

AD = 6 cm

Work out the difference in area between rectangle *ABCD* and rectangle *DAXY*.

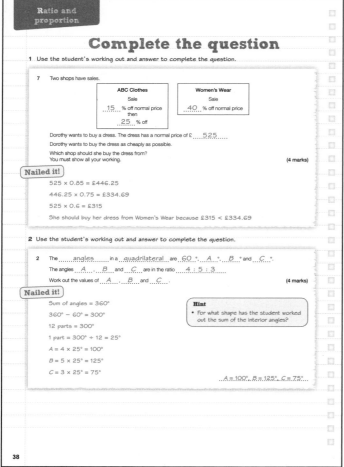

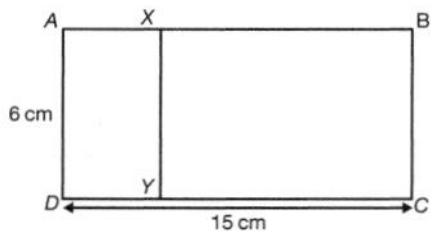

Hints
- First, work out the width of rectangle *DAXY*.
- Then, work out its area.

(3 marks)

[4] = 75.6 cm²

[2] 2.4 × 6 = 14.4 cm²

[1] $6 \times \frac{6}{15} = 2.4$ cm

[3] (15 × 6) − 14.4

2 Rearrange the working out into the most logical order by numbering each part.

16 Lisa is organising a charity event to raise money.
18% of the total money raised will cover the costs of the event.
The rest of the money raised will be given to a care home and to a school in the ratio 5 : 3

Lisa sells 1500 tickets at £39.50 each.

Work out the amount of money that Lisa expects to give to the care home and to the school.
You must show all your working. (5 marks)

[3] 8 parts = 48585

[5] 5 parts = 6073.125 × 5 and 3 parts = 6073.125 × 3

[1] 1500 × 39.50 = 59250

[4] 1 part = 6073.125

[2] 59250 × 0.82 = 48585

[6] £30365.63 and £18219.38

It can be just as useful to highlight parts of the question in maths and science as it is in English. There's often a lot of information within a short amount of writing.

Ratio and proportion

Complete the question

1 Use the student's working out and answer to complete the question.

7 Two shops have sales.

ABC Clothes	Women's Wear
Sale	Sale
15 % off normal price then 25 % off	40 % off normal price

Dorothy wants to buy a dress. The dress has a normal price of £ 525

Dorothy wants to buy the dress as cheaply as possible.

Which shop should she buy the dress from?
You must show all your working. (4 marks)

Nailed it!

525 × 0.85 = £446.25

446.25 × 0.75 = £334.69

525 × 0.6 = £315

She should buy her dress from Women's Wear because £315 < £334.69

2 Use the student's working out and answer to complete the question.

2 The angles in a quadrilateral are 60 °, *A* °, *B* ° and *C* °.

The angles *A*, *B* and *C* are in the ratio 4 : 5 : 3

Work out the values of *A*, *B* and *C*. (4 marks)

Nailed it!

Sum of angles = 360°

360° − 60° = 300°

12 parts = 300°

1 part = 300° ÷ 12 = 25°

A = 4 × 25° = 100°

B = 5 × 25° = 125°

C = 3 × 25° = 75°

Hint
- For what shape has the student worked out the sum of the interior angles?

A = 100°, *B* = 125°, *C* = 75°

Ratio and proportion

Complete the answer

1 Use the hint below to complete the student's answer so that it would be awarded 3 marks.

16 Govind has 36 white tiles and 12 black tiles.

The cost of each white tile was £2.50
The cost of each black tile was £4.50

Work out the ratio of the total cost of the white tiles to the total cost of the black tiles.
Give your answer in its simplest form. (3 marks)

36 × 2.50 = £90

12 × 4.50 = £54

Total cost of the white tiles : total cost of the black tiles

90 : 54 (÷2)

45 : 27 (÷9)

5 : 3

Hint
- First, find the total cost of the white tiles, and the total cost of the black tiles.

5 : 3

2 For each part of the question, complete the student's answer so that it would be awarded full marks.

9 Christine is going to the USA.
She wants to change some pounds to dollars.

A travel agent offers this deal.

Travel Money
Exchange rate: £1 = $1.35
£10 transaction charge

(a) Write an equation Christine can use to work out how many dollars (*D*) she will get for *P* pounds. (3 marks)

Transaction charge in dollars = 10 × 1.35

$D = 1.35P - 13.5$

$D = 1.35P - 13.5$

(b) Christine has £250
How many dollars can she get? (2 marks)

Using $D = 1.35P - 13.5$

$D = 1.35 \times 250 - 13.5$

$D = 324$

$ 324

3 Complete the student's answer so that it would be awarded 3 marks.

14 Aiden bought a car for £20000

The value of the car depreciated by 20% in the first year and then by 10% in the second year.

Work out the value of Aiden's car at the end of the two years. (3 marks)

End of first year = 20000 × 0.8 = 16000

End of second year = 16000 × 0.9 = 14400

£14400

Improve the answer

1 Write an improved answer that would be awarded 2 marks.

9 9 calculators cost £40.50
Work out the cost of 16 of these calculators. (2 marks)

The student has correctly started to work out the cost of one calculator, but has made a mistake in their calculation.

Nearly there

40.50 ÷ 9 = 45.00
16 × 45.00 = £720
£720

40.50 ÷ 9 = £4.50
£4.50 × 16 = £72
£72

2 Write an improved answer that would be awarded 2 marks.

13 Earl buys a new van for £15000
The value of the van depreciates at the rate of 24% per year.
After *n* years the value of the van is £5004.33
Find the value of *n*. (2 marks)

The student has found the decrease in price for the first year of *n* but has misunderstood the compound nature of depreciation.

Had a go

£15000 × 0.24 = £3600
£15000 − £3600 − £3600 = £7800
£7800 − £3600 = £4200
$n = 3$

£15000 × 0.76 = £11400
$£15000 \times 0.76^2 = £8664$
$£15000 \times 0.76^3 = £6584.64$
$£15000 \times 0.76^4 = £5004.33$
$n = 4$

3 Write an improved answer that would be awarded 3 marks.

18 Natalia travels to work by train.
The cost of her monthly train ticket increases by 12% to £235.20
Natalia's monthly pay increases by 6% to £535.60
Compare the increase in the amount of money Natalia has to pay for her monthly train ticket with the increase in her monthly pay. (3 marks)

Had a go

12% of £235.20 = 0.12 × 235.20 = £28.22
6% of £535.60 = 0.06 × 535.60 = £32.14
The monthly pay had a larger increase.

The student has misinterpreted what the amounts in the question represent.

100% + 12% = 112% = 1.12
£235.20 ÷ 1.12 = £210
Increase = £235.20 − £210 = £25.20
100% + 6% = 106% = 1.06
£535.60 ÷ 1.06 = £505.28
Increase = £535.60 − £505.28 = £30.32
The monthly pay had a larger increase.

40

Find the answer

1 Find the answer that would be awarded 2 marks. Choose A, B or C. Explain your choice.

6 A box contains only yellow pencils and green pencils.
The ratio of the number of yellow pencils to the number of green pencils is 4 : 11
What fraction of the pencils are yellow? (2 marks)

A $\frac{4}{11}$ B $\frac{4}{73}$ C $\frac{4}{15}$

Answer C would get 2 marks because the student has correctly written the number of yellow pencils as a fraction of the total number of pencils.

2 Find the answer that would be awarded 2 marks. Choose A, B or C. Explain your choice.

9 Luis has a piece of string that is 180 cm long.
He cuts the string into three lengths in the ratio 3 : 7 : 5
Work out the length, in centimetres, of the longest piece of string. (2 marks)

A	B	C
Total parts = 3 + 7 + 5 = 15 $\frac{3}{15} \times 180 = 36$ cm	Total parts = 3 + 7 + 5 = 15 $\frac{7}{15} \times 180 = 84$ cm	Total parts = 3 + 7 + 5 = 15 $\frac{15}{7} \times 180 = 386$ cm

Answer B would get 2 marks because the student has correctly identified that the longest piece of string is 7 parts long, and worked out its length in centimetres.

3 Use the hint below to find the answer that would be awarded 3 marks. Choose A, B or C. Explain your choice.

11 Philip is going on holiday to Denmark.
He needs to change some money.
Philip wants to change up to £400 into krone.
He wants as many 50 krone notes as possible.
The exchange rate is £1 = 8.37 krone.
How many 50 krone notes should he get? (3 marks)

Hint
- You can assume Philip changes £400

A	B	C
400 × 8.37 = 3348 3348 ÷ 50 = 66.96 67 notes	400 × 8.37 = 3348 3348 ÷ 50 = 66.96 66 notes	400 ÷ 50 = 8 8 × 8.4 = 67.2 67 notes

Answer B would get 3 marks because the student has correctly converted £400 to krone and then worked out the number of 50 krone notes this could include.

41

Complete the question

1 Use the student's working out and answer to complete each part of the question.

14 A scientist is investigating the population growth of a type of bacteria.
At the start of day 1, there are 50000 bacteria.
The scientist assumes that the population will increase at a constant rate of 15 % each day.
(a) Estimate the population of the bacteria at the end of day 4
Give your answer correct to 3 significant figures. (3 marks)

Nailed it!

100% + 15% = 115% = 1.15
$50000 \times (1.15)^4 = 87450.3125 = 87500$
87500

The scientist estimates that at the end of day 10 the population of the bacteria will be 202278
(b) The scientist's assumption about the rate of increase of the population is too high.
How might this affect his estimate for day 10? (1 mark)

Hint
- Think about what would happen if the population increased by 10% or 20% each day, for example.

Nailed it!

The population will be less than 202278 at the end of day 10

2 Use the student's working out and answer to complete the question.

10 Marcel wants to invest £ 35000 for 3 years in a bank.

Penn Bank	WV4 Bank
Compound interest 2 % for each year	Compound interest 4.2 % for the first year 0.8 % for each extra year

Which bank will give Marcel the most interest at the end of 3 years?
You must show all your working. (3 marks)

Nailed it!

$35000 \times 1.02^3 = 37142.28$
So 37142.28 − 35000 = £2142.28
$35000 \times 1.042 \times 1.008^2 = 37055.85$
So 37055.85 − 35000 = £2055.85
Penn Bank

42

Mark the answer

1 Use the mark scheme to assign a mark to the answer. Explain your decision.

15 Hassan and Roger are going to share £1250 in the ratio of their ages. The combined age of Hassan and Roger is 24 years. Roger is six years younger than Hassan.
Work out how much money Hassan and Roger each get. You must show all your working. (5 marks)

6 ÷ 2 = 3
Hassan's age = 24 ÷ 2 + 3 = 12 + 3 = 15
Roger's age = 24 ÷ 2 − 3 = 12 − 3 = 9
Ratio 15 : 9
Hassan = $\frac{9}{24} \times 1250 = £468.75$
Roger = $\frac{15}{24} \times 1250 = £781.25$
Hassan £468.75, Roger £781.25

If you're sharing in a ratio, add the amounts at the end to check you get the correct total.

Answer	Notes
Hassan £781.25 Roger £468.75	P1 start process to work out the age of Hassan or Roger e.g. 6 ÷ 2 = 3 or 24 ÷ 2 + 3 (= 15) or 24 ÷ 2 − 3 (= 9) P1 complete process to work out the ages of Hassan and Roger e.g. 24 ÷ 2 + 3 (= 15) and 24 ÷ 2 − 3 (= 9) P1 process to work out the amount of money for Hassan and Roger e.g. $\frac{\text{"15"}}{24} \times 1250 (= £781.25)$ or $\frac{\text{"9"}}{24} \times 1250 (= £468.75)$ A1 Hassan gets £781.25 A1 Roger gets £468.75

I would award the answer 3 out of 5 marks because the student has correctly found Hassan's and Roger's ages, gaining the first 2 marks. They have used a correct method to find the two amounts of money, gaining the third mark. They do not get the final 2 marks because they have mixed up the amount each receives.

2 Use the mark scheme to assign a mark to the answer. Explain your decision.

13 Adele buys a phone for £150 to sell in her shop. At Adele's shop, customers with a loyalty card get 10% off the full price. Adele wants to make a profit of 20% if a customer with a loyalty card buys the phone.
Work out how much Adele should charge for the phone at full price. (3 marks)

150 × 1.20 = 180
180 ÷ 0.9 = 200
£200

Answer	Notes
£200	P1 for a process to increase the price using 20% e.g. 150 × 1.2 (= 180) P1 for a process to increase the price using 10% e.g. "180" ÷ 0.9 A1 cao

I would award the answer 3 out of 3 marks because the student has correctly applied the percentage calculations in the correct order and has given a correct answer.

43

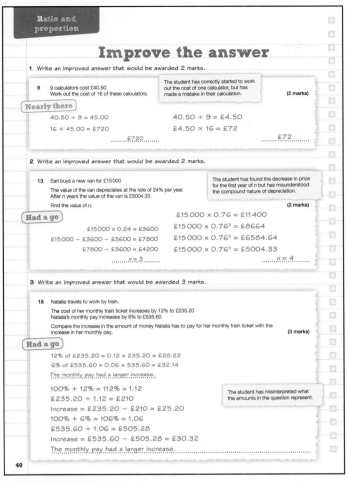

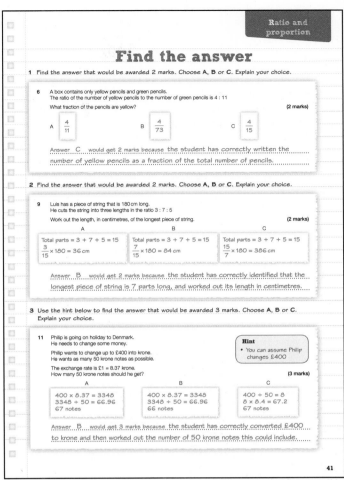

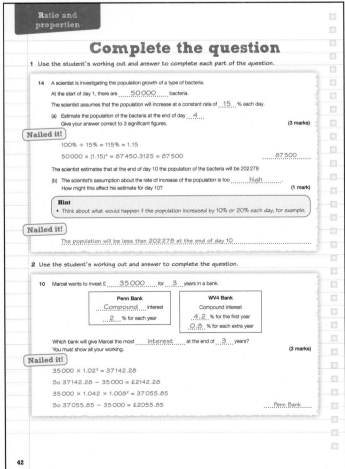

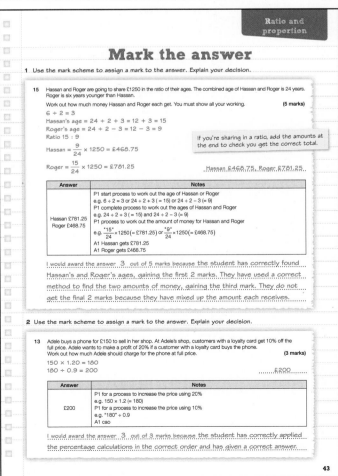

Re-order the answer

1 Rearrange the working out into the most logical order by numbering each part.

5 Melissa wants to buy a table.
She looks on the internet and finds two offers.

UK	France
£450	€500
No delivery charge	€20 for delivery

£1 = €1.10

Whose table is cheaper, including the delivery charge?
You must show your working. **(3 marks)**

[3] 450 and 473

[1] 500 + 20

[4] The table from the UK is cheaper.

[2] 520 ÷ 1.10 = 472.73

2 Rearrange the working out into the most logical order by numbering each part.

11 There are 240 counters in a box.
Each counter is either red or green.
There are three times as many green counters as red counters in the box.
Jacob takes 30% of the green counters from the box.
Work out the ratio of the number of red counters to the number of green counters now in the box.
Give your ratio in its simplest form. **(3 marks)**

[5] 10 : 21

[3] 0.7 × 180 = 126

[2] $\frac{3}{4}$ × 240 = 180

[1] red : green = 1 : 3

[4] 60 : 126

Complete the question

1 Use the student's working out and answer to complete the question.

14 Daniel and Hans share some money.
Daniel receives 30 %.
Hans' share is larger than Daniel's share.
Write Daniel's share : Hans' share as a ratio.
Give your answer in its simplest form. **(2 marks)**

Nailed it!

100% − 30% = 70%

30% : 70%

3 : 7

3 : 7

2 Use the student's working out and answer to complete the question.

8 In a fridge, there are 119 fruit-based pies.
There are 3 times as many apple pies as cherry pies and a quarter as many key lime pies as cherry pies.
How many of each type of pie are there in the fridge? **(3 marks)**

Nailed it!

3 : 1

1 : 0.25

3 : 1 : 0.25 so 12 : 4 : 1

17 parts = 119 so 1 part = 7

Apple = 12 × 7 = 84, cherry = 4 × 7 = 28 and key lime = 1 × 7 = 7

84 apple, 28 cherry, 7 key lime

3 Use the student's working out and answer to complete the question.

4 Joan bought a car for £ 16 000 .
Each year the value of the car depreciated by 15 %.
Work out the value of the car two years after she bought it. **(3 marks)**

Nailed it!

100% − 15% = 85% = 0.85

£16 000 × 0.85 × 0.85 = £11 560

£ 11 560

Complete the answer

1 Use the hints below to complete the student's answer so that it would be awarded 5 marks.

14 Here are the instructions for making a lemon drink.
"Mix 1 part of lemon squash with 5 parts of water."
Katrina is going to make lemon drinks for 30 children.
Each child is going to have 2 lemon drinks.
Each cup holds 300 millilitres of lemon drink.
A one-litre bottle of lemon squash costs £1.50

Hints
- First, work out how much lemon drink Katrina needs.
- Then work out how much of this is lemon squash.

Work out the total cost of the bottles of lemon squash Katrina needs to buy. (1 litre = 1000 millilitres) **(5 marks)**

Number of cups = 30 × 2 = 60

60 × 300 = 18 000 ml

18 000 ÷ 1000 = 18 litres

Lemon squash : water = 1 : 5

Lemon squash = $\frac{1}{6}$ × 18 = 3 litres

Number of bottles = 3

Cost of the bottles = 3 × £1.50 = £4.50

£ 4.50

2 Use the hint below to complete the student's answer so that it would be awarded 3 marks.

19 Ivanka is going to make some chocolate biscuits.
Here are the ingredients needed to make 8 chocolate biscuits.

Ingredients for 8 chocolate biscuits
50 g butter
25 g sugar
60 g flour
10 g cocoa

Hint
- How many biscuits does Ivanka have enough butter for? What about sugar, flour and cocoa?

Ivanka has:
175 g of butter
200 g of sugar
300 g of flour
60 g of cocoa

Work out the greatest number of chocolate biscuits that Ivanka can make with her ingredients.
You must show your working. **(3 marks)**

Butter = 175 ÷ 50 = 3.5 Number of biscuits with butter = 3.5 × 8 = 28

Sugar = 200 ÷ 25 = 8 Number of biscuits with sugar = 8 × 8 = 64

Flour = 300 ÷ 60 = 5 Number of biscuits with flour = 5 × 8 = 40

Cocoa = 60 ÷ 10 = 6 Number of biscuits with cocoa = 6 × 8 = 48

Maximum number of biscuits = 28

Improve the answer

1 Use the hint below to write an improved answer that would be awarded 2 marks.

7 Here are four graphs.

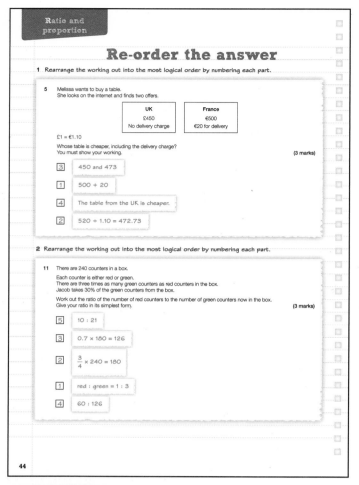

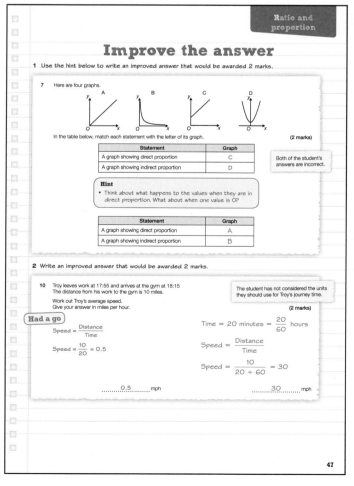

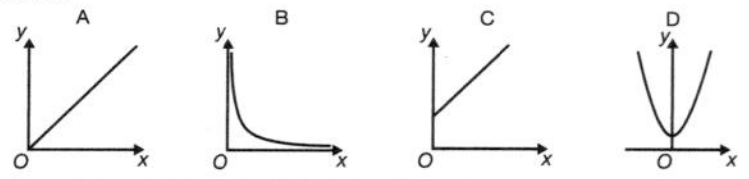

In the table below, match each statement with the letter of its graph. **(2 marks)**

Statement	Graph
A graph showing direct proportion	C
A graph showing indirect proportion	D

Both of the student's answers are incorrect.

Hint
- Think about what happens to the values when they are in direct proportion. What about when one value is 0?

Statement	Graph
A graph showing direct proportion	A
A graph showing indirect proportion	B

2 Write an improved answer that would be awarded 2 marks.

10 Troy leaves work at 17:55 and arrives at the gym at 18:15
The distance from his work to the gym is 10 miles.
Work out Troy's average speed.
Give your answer in miles per hour. **(2 marks)**

The student has not considered the units they should use for Troy's journey time.

Had a go

Speed = $\frac{\text{Distance}}{\text{Time}}$

Speed = $\frac{10}{20}$ = 0.5

0.5 mph

Time = 20 minutes = $\frac{20}{60}$ hours

Speed = $\frac{\text{Distance}}{\text{Time}}$

Speed = $\frac{10}{20 \div 60}$ = 30

30 mph

Ratio and proportion

Find the answer

1 For each part of the question, find the answer that would be awarded full marks. Choose **A**, **B** or **C**. Explain your choice.

11 Tony uses his van to deliver parcels.
He uses this graph to work out what to charge his customers.

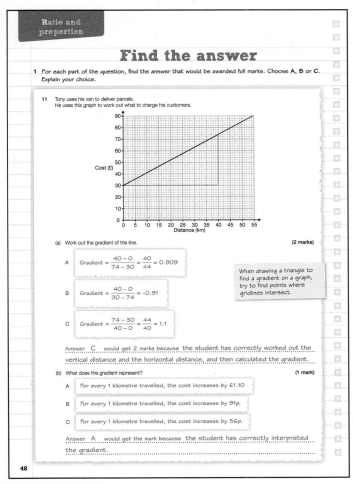

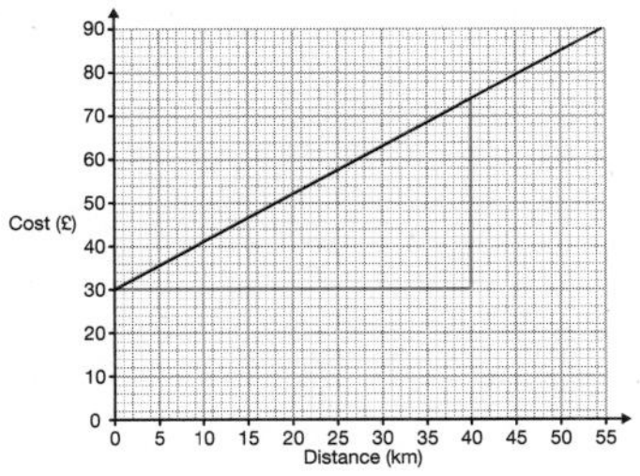

(a) Work out the gradient of the line. **(2 marks)**

A Gradient $= \frac{40-0}{74-30} = \frac{40}{44} = 0.909$

B Gradient $= \frac{40-0}{30-74} = -0.91$

C Gradient $= \frac{74-30}{40-0} = \frac{44}{40} = 1.1$

When drawing a triangle to find a gradient on a graph, try to find points where gridlines intersect.

Answer C would get 2 marks because the student has correctly worked out the vertical distance and the horizontal distance, and then calculated the gradient.

(b) What does the gradient represent? **(1 mark)**

A For every 1 kilometre travelled, the cost increases by £1.10

B For every 1 kilometre travelled, the cost increases by 91p.

C For every 1 kilometre travelled, the cost increases by 56p.

Answer A would get the mark because the student has correctly interpreted the gradient.

48

Ratio and proportion

Mark the answer

1 Use the mark scheme to assign a mark to the answer. Explain your decision.

15 A tin of beans costs 55p. A shop has a special offer.

Buy 3 tins of beans and get 1 free.

Work out the cost of 20 tins of beans. **(3 marks)**

Tins : free tins = 3 : 1

Number of tins to pay for $= \frac{3}{4} \times 20 = 15$

Cost of the tins $= 15 \times 55 = 825$

£ 825

Answer	Notes
£8.25	P1 process to work out the number of tins e.g. 20 ÷ 4 × 3 (= 15) or (3 + 1) + (3 + 1) + (3 + 1) + (3 + 1) + (3 + 1) = (15 + 5) P1 process to work out the cost of the tins e.g. "15" × 55 (= 825) or "15" × 0.55 (= 8.25) A1 cao

I would award the answer 2 out of 3 marks because the student has worked out the number of tins that would be paid for and their cost. They lose the final mark because they have not converted their answer to pounds.

2 Use the mark scheme to assign a mark to the answer. Explain your decision.

12 Anders and Ravi share £4800 in the ratio 5 : 7
Anders gives half of his share to Saul.
Ravi gives one quarter of his share to Saul.
Write the ratio of the amount Saul receives to the total amount. Give your answer in its simplest form. **(4 marks)**

Anders $= \frac{5}{12} \times 4800 = 2000$ and Ravi $= \frac{7}{12} \times 4800 = 2800$

$2000 \div 2 = 1000$ and $2800 \div 4 = 700$

Saul $= 1000 + 700 = 1700$

Ratio $= 1700 : 4800$

Answer	Notes
17 : 48	P1 for a process to work out Anders' and Ravi's shares e.g 4800 ÷ 12 × 5 (= 2000) and 4800 ÷ 12 × 7 (= 2800) P1 for a process to work out the amount given to Saul e.g. "2000" ÷ 2 (= 1000) and "2800" ÷ 4 (= 700) P1 for a process to work out the total amount given to Saul e.g. "1000" + "700" = (1700) A1 cao

I would award the answer 3 out of 4 marks because the student has worked out the ratio correctly, but has not written it in its simplest form, losing the final mark.

49

Ratio and proportion

Re-order the answer

1 Rearrange the working out into the most logical order by numbering each part. Use the hint to help.

2 Sophia makes a scale model of a ship.
She uses a scale of 1 : 25
The length of Sophia's model ship is 48 cm.
Cassius makes a scale model of the same ship.
He uses a scale of 1 : 40
What is the difference in length of the two model ships? **(3 marks)**

4 = 18 cm

2 1200 ÷ 40 = 30

1 25 × 48 = 1200

3 48 − 30

Hint
- First, work out the length of the real ship.

2 Rearrange the working out into the most logical order by numbering each part. Use the hint to help.

13 Here is a map showing Penn and Basingstoke.

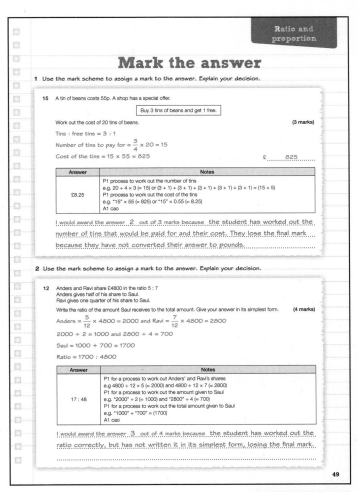

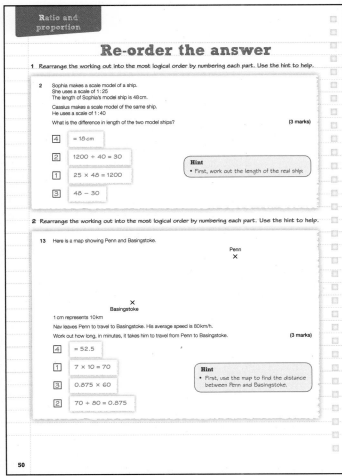

1 cm represents 10 km
Nav leaves Penn to travel to Basingstoke. His average speed is 80 km/h.
Work out how long, in minutes, it takes him to travel from Penn to Basingstoke. **(3 marks)**

4 = 52.5

1 7 × 10 = 70

3 0.875 × 60

2 70 ÷ 80 = 0.875

Hint
- First, use the map to find the distance between Penn and Basingstoke.

50

Ratio and proportion

Complete the answer

1 Use the hint below to complete the student's answer so that it would be awarded 3 marks.

21 a is inversely proportional to b.
When $b = 18$, $a = 6$
Find the value of a when $b = 16$ **(3 marks)**

$a \propto \frac{1}{b}$

$a = \frac{k}{b}$

$k = 18 \times 6 = 108$

$a = \frac{108}{b} = \frac{108}{16} = 6.75$

6.75

Hint
- Write an equation connecting a and b using k, the constant of proportionality. Solve for k.

2 Use the hints below to complete the student's answer so that it would be awarded 3 marks.

11 A box contains red, blue and yellow counters.
The ratio of the number of red counters to the number of blue counters is 7 : 6
The ratio of the number of blue counters to the number of yellow counters is 4 : 3
The total number of counters is 560
How many blue counters are there in the box? **(3 marks)**

7 : 6 = 14 : 12

4 : 3 = 12 : 9

Red : blue : yellow = 14 : 12 : 9

Total number of parts = 14 + 12 + 9 = 35

Number of blue counters $= \frac{12}{35} \times 560 = 192$

192

Hints
- First, rewrite both ratios so that the number of parts representing blue counters is the same.
- You can then combine the two ratios into one three-part ratio.

3 Use the hints below to complete the student's answer so that it would be awarded 3 marks.

4 Given that
$4x - 7 : 3 = 2x + 3 : 5$
find the exact value of x. **(3 marks)**

$\frac{4x-7}{3} = \frac{2x+3}{5}$

$5(4x - 7) = 3(2x + 3)$

$20x - 35 = 6x + 9$

$20x - 6x = 9 + 35$

$14x = 44$

$x = \frac{44}{14} = \frac{22}{7}$

$\frac{22}{7}$

Hints
- Rewrite the ratios as fractions.
- Then, solve the equation to find x.

51

Ratio and proportion

Improve the answer

1 Write an improved answer that would be awarded 3 marks.

19 y is proportional to x.
When $x = 6$, $y = 150$
Work out the value of y when $x = 4$ (3 marks)

Nearly there

$y \propto x$
$y = kx$
$150 = k \times 6$
$k = 6 \div 150$
$k = 0.04$
$y = 0.04x$
$y = 0.04 \times 4$
$y = 0.16$

0.16

The student has set up an equation linking x and y, but has made a mistake in their calculation of k.

$y \propto x$
$y = kx$
$150 = k \times 6$
$k = 150 \div 6$
$k = 25$
$y = 25x$
$y = 25 \times 4$
$y = 100$

100

2 Write an improved answer that would be awarded 3 marks.

9 The diagram shows a solid triangular prism.
The prism is made from metal.
The mass of the metal prism is 924 grams.
Work out the density, in grams per cm³, of the metal. (3 marks)

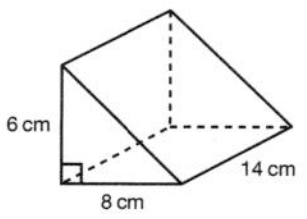

Nearly there

Volume $= \frac{1}{2} \times 6 \times 8 \times 14$
$= 336$ cm³
Density $= \frac{\text{Volume}}{\text{Mass}}$
$= \frac{336}{924} = 0.364$

0.364 g/cm³

The student has correctly worked out the volume of the prism, but has incorrectly written the formula for density.

Volume $= \frac{1}{2} \times 6 \times 8 \times 14$
$= 336$ cm³
Density $= \frac{\text{Mass}}{\text{Volume}}$
$= \frac{924}{336} = 2.75$

2.75 g/cm³

Ratio and proportion

Complete the answer

1 Use the hints below to complete the student's answer so that it would be awarded 3 marks.

15 Ian is building a wall.
When he uses 750 bricks, the wall is 6 metres long and 1.25 metres high.
Ian wants the finished wall to be 10 metres long and 1.25 metres high.
How many more bricks does Ian need to finish the wall? (3 marks)

1 m: $750 \div 6 = 125$
10 m: $125 \times 10 = 1250$ bricks
Number of bricks needed $= 1250 - 750 = 500$

500

Hints
- Work out how many bricks Ian uses per metre of wall.
- Then, work out how many bricks Ian needs for the whole wall.
- Finally, work out how many more bricks Ian needs.

2 Use the hint below to complete the student's answer so that it would be awarded 4 marks.

8 A shop sells packs of kitchen rolls in three sizes.
A pack of 8 kitchen rolls costs £4.40
A pack of 6 kitchen rolls costs £3.33
A pack of 5 kitchen rolls costs £2.80
Which pack gives the best value for money?
You must show all your working. (4 marks)

Hint
- Work out the cost per roll for each pack.

Pack of 8: $440 \div 8 = 55$p each
Pack of 6: $333 \div 6 = 55.5$p each
Pack of 5: $280 \div 5 = 56$p each

Pack of 8 is the best value for money.

3 Use the hints below to complete the student's answer so that it would be awarded 3 marks.

12 Gil sells some bags of carrots and bags of turnips at his farm shop.
In one week, he sells three times as many bags of carrots as bags of turnips.
The total number of bags of carrots and bags of turnips he sells is 40
He sells the bags of carrots and bags of turnips for £52 in total. He sells each bag of carrots for £1.15
Work out the cost of each bag of turnips. (3 marks)

Carrots : turnips = 3 : 1
4 parts = 40
1 part $= 40 \div 4 = 10$
Number of bags of carrots $= 3 \times 10 = 30$
Total cost of carrots $= 30 \times £1.15 = £34.50$
Number of bags of turnips $= 40 - 30 = 10$
Total cost of turnips $= £52 - £34.50 = £17.50$
Cost of a bag of turnips $= £17.50 \div 10 = £1.75$

£1.75

Hints
- Work out how many bags of carrots and how many bags of turnips Gil sells.
- Work out the total cost of the bags of carrots Gil sells.
- Then, work out the cost of the turnips.

Geometry and measures

Improve the answer

1 For each part of the question, write an improved answer that would be awarded full marks.

11 (a) Describe fully the single transformation which maps triangle **A** onto triangle **B**. (3 marks)

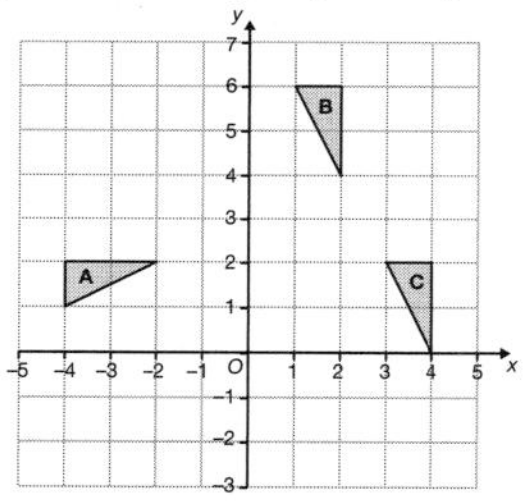

Nearly there

Rotation 90°

Rotation 90° centre (1, 1) clockwise

The student has correctly identified that this is a rotation of 90°. They have not stated the centre of rotation or the direction.

(b) Describe fully the single transformation which maps triangle **C** onto triangle **B**. (2 marks)

Transformation of $\begin{pmatrix}-2\\4\end{pmatrix}$

Translation of $\begin{pmatrix}-2\\4\end{pmatrix}$

The student has used the wrong word to describe the transformation.

2 Write an improved answer that would be awarded 2 marks.

16 Using $\mathbf{a} = \begin{pmatrix}5\\-2\end{pmatrix}$ and $\mathbf{b} = \begin{pmatrix}4\\3\end{pmatrix}$
Work out $\mathbf{b} - 3\mathbf{a}$ (2 marks)

Nearly there

$\mathbf{b} - 3\mathbf{a} = \begin{pmatrix}4\\3\end{pmatrix} - 3\begin{pmatrix}5\\-2\end{pmatrix} = \begin{pmatrix}4-15\\3-6\end{pmatrix} = \begin{pmatrix}-11\\-3\end{pmatrix}$

$\begin{pmatrix}-11\\-3\end{pmatrix}$

The student has set the calculation up correctly, but has made a mistake with the signs.

$\mathbf{b} - 3\mathbf{a} = \begin{pmatrix}4\\3\end{pmatrix} - 3\begin{pmatrix}5\\-2\end{pmatrix} = \begin{pmatrix}4-15\\3-(-6)\end{pmatrix} = \begin{pmatrix}-11\\9\end{pmatrix}$

$\begin{pmatrix}-11\\9\end{pmatrix}$

Geometry and measures

Find the answer

1 Find the answer that would be awarded 2 marks. Choose A, B or C. Explain your choice.

15 Find the size of the angle marked x. Give a reason for your answer. (2 marks)

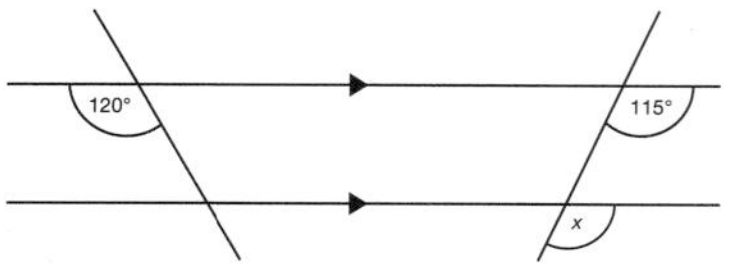

A 115° because corresponding angles are equal.

B 120° because corresponding angles are equal.

C 115° because F angles are equal.

Answer A would get 2 marks because the student has correctly worked out the angle and has given a correct mathematical reason.

2 Find the answer that would be awarded 2 marks. Choose A, B or C. Explain your choice.

17 ABC is a right-angled triangle.
$BC = 12.7$ cm
$AB = 6.9$ cm
Calculate the size of the angle marked x.
Give your answer correct to 1 decimal place. (2 marks)

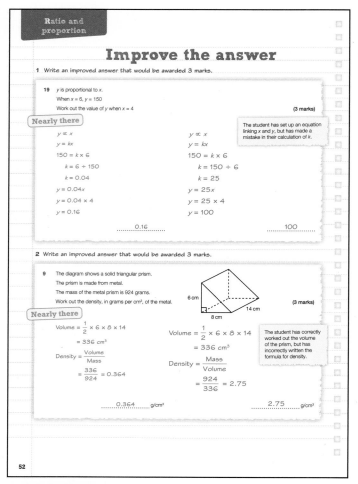

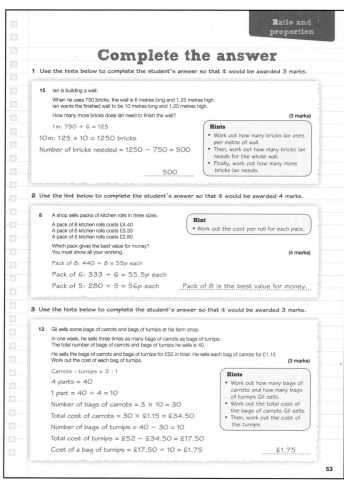

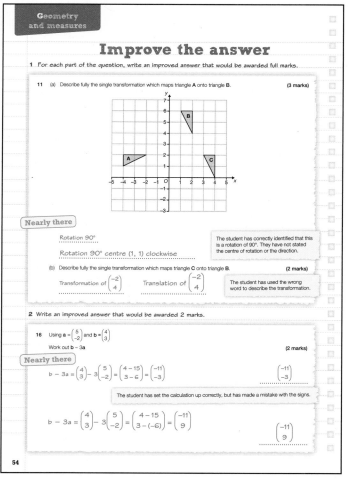

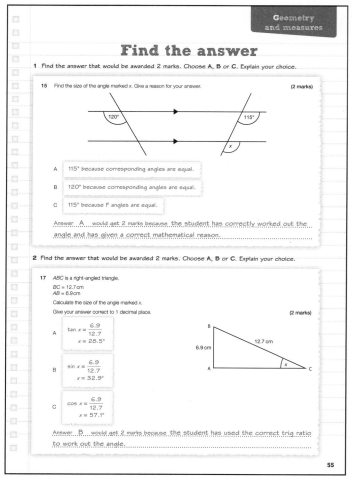

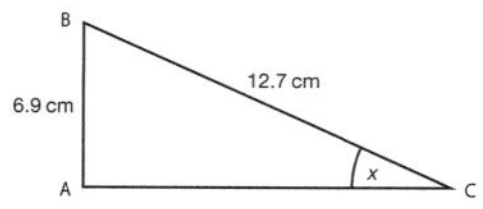

A $\tan x = \frac{6.9}{12.7}$, $x = 28.5°$

B $\sin x = \frac{6.9}{12.7}$, $x = 32.9°$

C $\cos x = \frac{6.9}{12.7}$, $x = 57.1°$

Answer B would get 2 marks because the student has used the correct trig ratio to work out the angle.

Mark the answer

1 Use the mark scheme to assign a mark to the answer. Explain your decision.

7 A circle has a diameter of 15 cm.

Work out the area of the circle.
Give your answer correct to 3 significant figures. (2 marks)

Area = πr^2

$= \pi \times 15 \times 15$

$= 707\ cm^2$

......707...... cm^2

Answer	Notes
177 cm^2	M1 for $\pi \times 7.5 \times 7.5$ A1 for 177

I would award the answer ...0... out of 2 marks because ...the student has not worked out the radius and their final answer is wrong.

2 Use the mark scheme to assign a mark to the answer. Explain your decision.

12 Work out the value of x.
Give your answer correct to 3 significant figures. (4 marks)

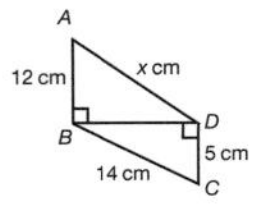

$BD^2 + 5^2 = 14^2$

$BD^2 + 25 = 196$

$BD^2 = 196 - 25$

$BD^2 = 171$

$BD = \sqrt{171}$

$BD = 13.1$

$x^2 = 13.1^2 + 12^2$

$x^2 = 171.61 + 144$

$x^2 = 315.61$

$x = \sqrt{315.61}$

$x = 17.8$

......17.8...... cm

Answer	Notes
17.7	P1 process to find BD^2 e.g. $14^2 - 5^2$ (= 171) P1 process to find x^2 e.g. "171" + 12^2 P1 process to find x e.g. $\sqrt{(\text{"171"}+12^2)}$ A1 cao

I would award the answer ...3... out of 4 marks because ...the student has used a correct method, but has rounded an answer prematurely – this has affected the accuracy of the final answer.

Re-order the answer

1 Rearrange the working out into the most logical order by numbering each part.

5 The diagram shows a podium in the shape of a circle.

The podium has a diameter of 1.8 m.

Rigby is going to put bunting around the edge of the podium.
The bunting is sold in 0.5 metre rolls.

How many rolls of bunting does Rigby need to buy?
You must show all your working. (3 marks)

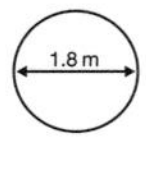

[4] = 12

[2] $1.8\pi \div 0.5$

[1] Length = $\pi \times 1.8$

[3] = 11.31

2 Rearrange the working out into the most logical order by numbering each part.

20 $ABCD$ is a quadrilateral.

DCE is a straight line.

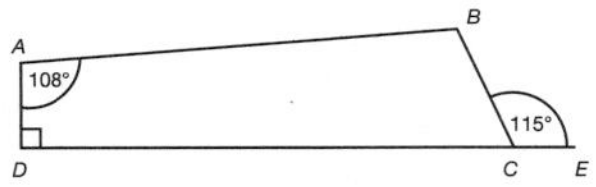

Work out the size of angle ABC.

You must give a reason for each stage of your working. (4 marks)

[2] because angles on a straight line add up to 180°.

[4] because angles in a quadrilateral add up to 360°.

[1] 180° − 115° = 65°

[3] 360° − 90° − 65° − 108° = 97°

Complete the question

1 Use the student's working out and answer to complete the question.

9 The diagram represents a triangular patio ABC.

A statue is going to be placed on the patio so that it is:

- nearer to ...AB... than to ...AC...
- within ...5... metres of point ...A...

On the diagram, shade the region where the statue may be placed. (3 marks)

Nailed it!

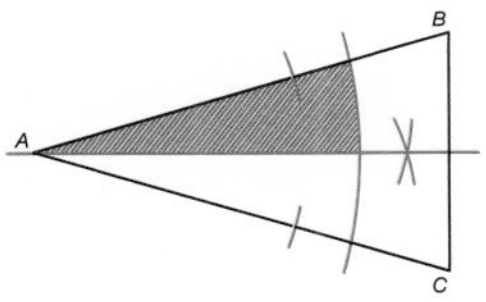

1 cm represents 1 m

2 Use the student's working out and answer to complete the question.

12 The diagram shows a right-angled ...triangular... prism A and a ...cube... B.

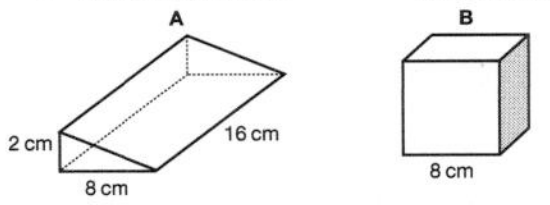

Show that the ...volume... of ...B... is ...4... times the ...volume... of ...A... (3 marks)

Nailed it!

$8 \times 8 \times 8 = 512\ cm^3$

$\frac{1}{2} \times 2 \times 8 \times 16 = 128\ cm^3$

$512 = 4 \times 128$

3 Use the student's working out and answer to complete the question.

5 Work out the ...sum... of the ...interior... angles of a ...hexagon... (2 marks)

Nailed it!

Hint
- Think about what you know about angles and polygons.

$(6 - 2) \times 180° = 4 \times 180°$

$= 720°$

......720...... °

Mark the answer

1 Use the mark scheme to assign a mark to the answer. Explain your decision.

22 The diagram shows the floor plan of a stage.

The floor is in the shape of a rectangle $ABCD$ and a semicircle.

CD = 3.4 m
BC = 2.8 m

Sam is going to paint the floor with one coat of paint.

The paint is sold in tins.
One tin will cover 2.25 m^2.
One tin normally costs £18.50

Sam receives a discount of 12% on each tin of paint.
Work out the total cost of the tins of paint. (6 marks)

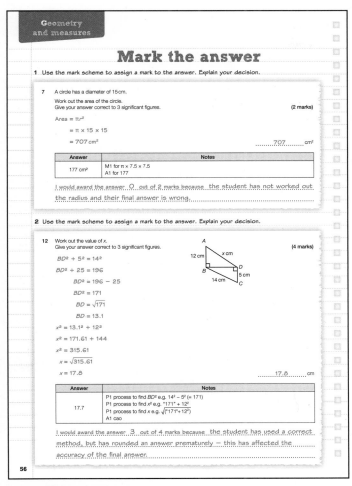

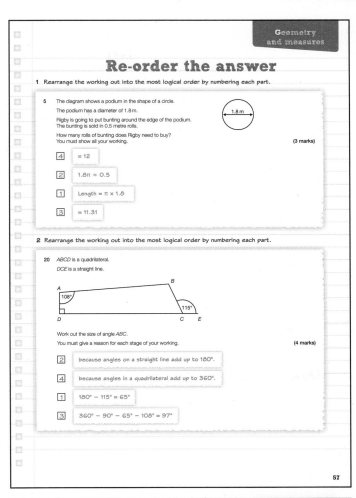

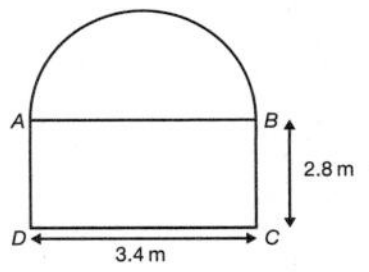

Radius of circle = 3.4 ÷ 2 = 1.7

Area of semicircle = (π × 1.7 × 1.7) ÷ 2 = 4.5396 = 4.54 m^2

Area of rectangle = 3.4 × 2.8 = 9.52 m^2

Total area = 4.54 + 9.52 = 14.06 m^2

Number of tins = 14.06 ÷ 2.25 = 6.249

12% of £18.50 = 12 ÷ 100 × 18.50 = £2.22

Cost of one tin of paint = 18.50 − 2.22 = £16.28

Total cost = 6 × 16.28 = £97.68

£ ......97.68......

Even if your final answer is wrong, you might still get some method marks so make sure you always show your working.

Answer	Notes
£113.96	P1 process to find the area of the semicircle or circle e.g. $\pi \times 1.7 \times 1.7$ (= 9.079) or ($\pi \times 1.7 \times 1.7$) ÷ 2 (= 4.54) P1 process to find the total area of the stage e.g. "4.54" + (3.4 × 2.8 = (9.52)) (= 14.06) P1 process to find the number of tins e.g. "14.06" ÷ 2.25 (= 6.249) P1 process to find cost of the total number of tins or uses discount to find cost of one tin e.g. "7" × 18.50 or 0.88 × 18.50 P1 process to find total cost e.g. "7" × 18.50 × 0.88 A1 cao

I would award the answer ...5... out of 6 marks because ...the student has correctly worked out the area of the stage to gain the first 2 marks. The student also gets the next 2 marks for correctly finding the number of tins and the discounted price of the paint. The student uses a correct process to work out the cost of the paint, gaining 1 more mark, but they have incorrectly rounded down to 6 so the final answer is wrong, and so they lose the final mark.

Complete the answer

1 Use the hint below to complete the student's answer so that it would be awarded 3 marks.

17 Here is a triangular frame *ABC*.

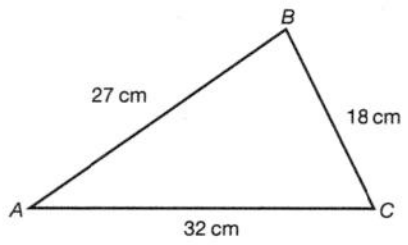

Mario makes a larger, similar triangular frame.
The shortest side is 81 cm.

Work out the total length of wire needed for the larger triangular frame. **(3 marks)**

> **Hint**
> • Find the scale factor and apply it to the perimeter of the given triangle.

Scale factor = 81 ÷ 18 = 4.5

Perimeter of given triangle = 18 + 27 + 32 = 77

Length of wire = 77 × 4.5 = 346.5 ....346.5........ cm

2 Use the hint below to complete the student's answer so that it would be awarded 3 marks.

16 The diagram shows a quarter of a circle with centre *O* and radius 5.2 cm.
AB is a chord of the circle.

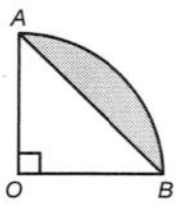

Calculate the area of the shaded segment.
Give your answer correct to 3 significant figures. **(3 marks)**

> **Hint**
> • Find the area of the quarter circle and the area of the triangle.

Area of circle = π × 5.2 × 5.2 = 84.9487 cm²

Area of quarter circle = 84.9487 ÷ 4 = 21.24 cm²

Area of triangle = $\frac{1}{2}$ × 5.2 × 5.2 = 13.52 cm²

Shaded area = 21.24 − 13.52 = 7.72 cm² ....7.72........ cm²

I write any measurements on the diagram if they are not already shown.

Improve the answer

1 Write an improved answer that would be awarded 3 marks.

13 Avi is a salesman.

Avi's journey from his home to his office is 75 km.
The journey takes 1 hour 10 minutes.

Work out his average speed in km/h.
Give your answer correct to 3 significant figures. **(3 marks)**

Nearly there

Speed = $\frac{\text{Distance}}{\text{Time}}$

= $\frac{75}{1.10}$ = 68.2

........68.2........ km/h

The student has converted the time Avi's journey takes into hours incorrectly.

Time = 70 minutes = $\frac{70}{60}$ hours

Speed = $\frac{\text{Distance}}{\text{Time}}$

= $\frac{75}{70 \div 60}$ = 64.3 km/h

........64.3........ km/h

2 For each part of the question, write an improved answer that would be awarded full marks.

14 The diagram shows part of a map.

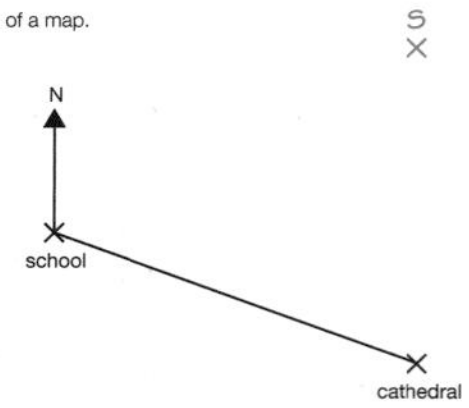

(a) Find the bearing of the cathedral from the school. **(1 mark)**

Had a go

........250........ °

The student appears to have read the wrong scale on their protractor.

........110........ °

The scale of the map is 1 cm represents 2.5 km.
A shop is 12.5 km due North of the cathedral.

(b) On the diagram, mark the position of the shop with a cross (×).
Label your cross S. **(2 marks)**

12.5 × 2.5 = 31.25 cm

The student has used the scale factor incorrectly and not marked the position of the shop on the map.

12.5 ÷ 2.5 = 5 cm

Find the answer

1 For each part of the question, find the answer that would be awarded the mark. Choose **A**, **B** or **C**. Explain your choice.

12 The diagram shows a solid triangular prism.

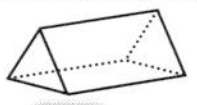

(a) Write down the number of faces. **(1 mark)**

A 5 B 6 C 9

Answer ...A... would get the mark because the student has correctly identified the number of faces.

(b) Write down the number of edges. **(1 mark)**

A 5 B 6 C 9

Answer ...C... would get the mark because the student has correctly identified the number of edges.

(c) Write down the number of vertices. **(1 mark)**

A 5 B 6 C 9

Answer ...B... would get the mark because the student has correctly identified the number of vertices.

2 For each part of the question, find the answer that would be awarded the mark. Choose **A**, **B** or **C**. Explain your choice.

13 Here is a quadrilateral.

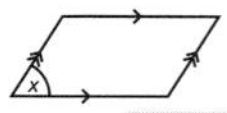

(a) Write down the mathematical name for this shape. **(1 mark)**

A Rectangle B Parallelogram C Rhombus

Answer ...B... would get the mark because the shape has two pairs of parallel lines, no right angles, and not all sides are the same length, so it is a parallelogram.

(b) Write down the mathematical name for the angle marked *x*. **(1 mark)**

A Acute B Obtuse C Reflex

Answer ...A... would get the mark because the angle is smaller than 90°, so it is acute.

Mark the answer

1 Use the mark scheme to assign a mark to the answer. Explain your decision.

19 The diagram shows a **solid** hemisphere.
The diameter of the hemisphere is 12 cm.
Find the total surface area of the solid hemisphere.
Give your answer in terms of π. **(3 marks)**

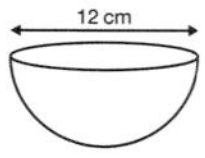

Surface area = $\frac{4\pi r^2}{2}$ + πr² = 3πr² = 3 × π × 6²

= 339 cm²

........339 cm²........

Answer	Notes
108π	M1 for 2πr² + πr² or 3πr² M1 for 3 × π × 6² A1 cao

I would award the answer ...2... out of 3 marks because the student has correctly used the formulae for the surface area of a sphere and the area of a circle, gaining the first 2 marks. They lose the final mark because they have not left the answer in terms of π.

2 Use the mark scheme to assign a mark to the answer. Explain your decision.

12 *ABCD* is a parallelogram.
E is the point where the diagonals *AC* and *BD* meet.
Prove that triangle *AED* is congruent to triangle *BEC*. **(3 marks)**

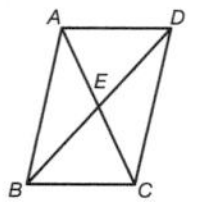

Angle *BCA* = angle *DAC*

AD = *BC*

Answer	Notes
Complete proof	M1 begins proof that angle *DAC* = angle *BCA* M1 *AD* = *BC* because opposite sides of a parallelogram are equal A1 completes proof e.g. alternate angles are equal and reference to ASA

I would award the answer ...1... out of 3 marks because the student has written down an equivalent statement, gaining the first mark, but they have not provided an explanation for why *AD* = *BC*, and has not completed the proof.

Geometry and measures

Find the answer

1 For each part of the question, find the answer that would be awarded the mark. Choose **A**, **B** or **C**. Explain your choice.

13 Here are five triangles drawn on a square grid.

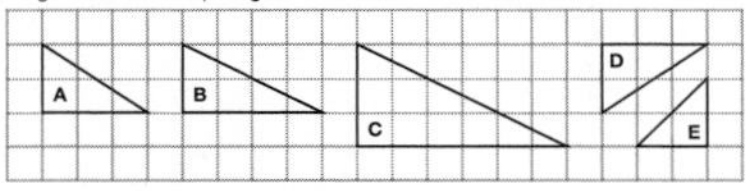

(a) Write down the letters of the two triangles that are congruent. **(1 mark)**

A: A and D B: D and E C: B and C

Answer A would get the mark because the student has remembered that congruent shapes are the same size as well as the same shape. They have identified the correct triangles.

One of the triangles is similar to triangle **B**.

(b) Write down the letter of this triangle. **(1 mark)**

A: A B: C C: E

Answer B would get the mark because the student has correctly identified the triangle with sides in the same ratio as triangle B.

2 For each part of the question, find the answer that would be awarded the mark. Choose **A**, **B** or **C**. Explain your choice.

5 *A* and *B* are points on a circle.

Write down the mathematical name for

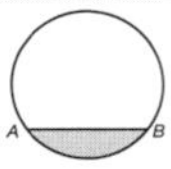

(a) the line *AB*. **(1 mark)**

A: Chord B: Tangent C: Diameter

Answer A would get the mark because the student has correctly recalled that a straight line joining two points on a circle is a chord.

(b) the shaded region. **(1 mark)**

A: Arc length B: Sector C: Segment

Answer C would get the mark because the student has correctly recalled that a part of a circle bound by an arc length and a chord is a segment.

Geometry and measures

Complete the answer

1 Use the hint below to complete the student's answer so that it would be awarded 2 marks.

10 The diagram shows three points, *A*, *B* and *C*, on a grid.

On the diagram, complete the rectangle *ABCD*. **(2 marks)**

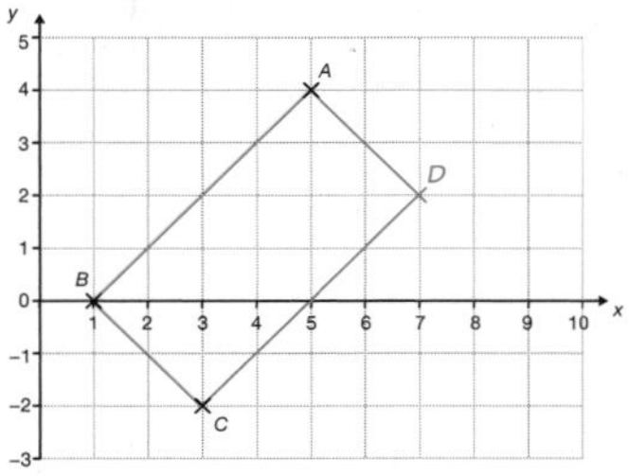

Hint
- Count squares to find the position of point *D*. Don't forget to label it.

2 Use the hint below to complete the student's answer so that it would be awarded 2 marks.

18 The front elevation and the plan for a prism are shown.

Front elevation

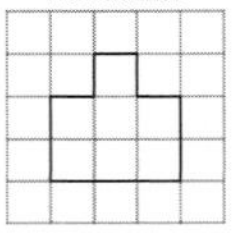

Plan

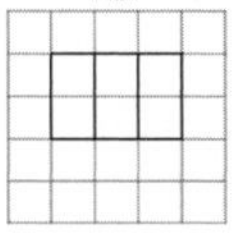

On the grid below, draw the side elevation of the prism. **(2 marks)**

Side

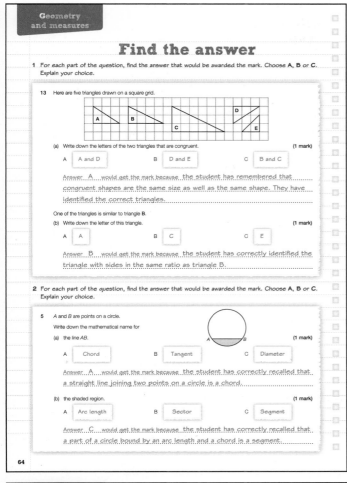

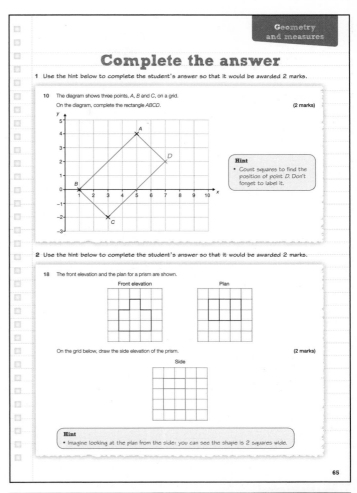

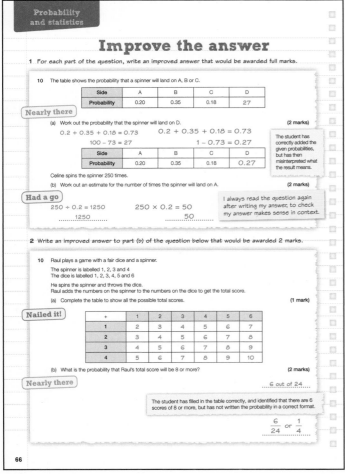

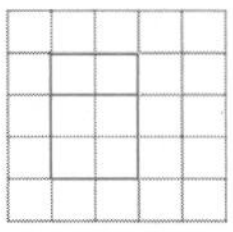

Hint
- Imagine looking at the plan from the side: you can see the shape is 2 squares wide.

Probability and statistics

Improve the answer

1 For each part of the question, write an improved answer that would be awarded full marks.

10 The table shows the probability that a spinner will land on A, B or C.

Side	A	B	C	D
Probability	0.20	0.35	0.18	27

Nearly there

(a) Work out the probability that the spinner will land on D. **(2 marks)**

0.2 + 0.35 + 0.18 = 0.73
100 − 73 = 27

$0.2 + 0.35 + 0.18 = 0.73$
$1 - 0.73 = 0.27$

Side	A	B	C	D
Probability	0.20	0.35	0.18	0.27

The student has correctly added the given probabilities, but has then misinterpreted what the result means.

Celine spins the spinner 250 times.

(b) Work out an estimate for the number of times the spinner will land on A. **(2 marks)**

Had a go

250 ÷ 0.2 = 1250
1250

$250 \times 0.2 = 50$
50

I always read the question again after writing my answer, to check my answer makes sense in context.

2 Write an improved answer to part (b) of the question below that would be awarded 2 marks.

10 Raul plays a game with a fair dice and a spinner.

The spinner is labelled 1, 2, 3 and 4
The dice is labelled 1, 2, 3, 4, 5 and 6

He spins the spinner and throws the dice.
Raul adds the numbers on the spinner to the numbers on the dice to get the total score.

(a) Complete the table to show all the possible total scores. **(1 mark)**

Nailed it!

+	1	2	3	4	5	6
1	2	3	4	5	6	7
2	3	4	5	6	7	8
3	4	5	6	7	8	9
4	5	6	7	8	9	10

(b) What is the probability that Raul's total score will be 8 or more? **(2 marks)**

Nearly there

6 out of 24

The student has filled in the table correctly, and identified that there are 6 scores of 8 or more, but has not written the probability in a correct format.

$\frac{6}{24}$ or $\frac{1}{4}$

Probability and statistics

Find the answer

1 For each part of the question, find the answer that would be awarded the mark. Choose **A**, **B** or **C**. Explain your choice.

7 Li has a 3-sided spinner.
The sides of the spinner are numbered 10, 20 and 30

(a) Li spins the spinner once.
Write down the word that best describes the probability that the spinner will land on the number 40 **(1 mark)**

A: Certain B: Even C: Impossible

Answer C would get the mark because the student has identified that the spinner will never land on 40, as 40 is not on the spinner.

(b) Write down the word that best describes the probability that the spinner will land on an even number. **(1 mark)**

A: Certain B: Even C: Impossible

Answer A would get the mark because the student has identified that 10, 20 and 30 are all even numbers and so the spinner will always land on an even number.

2 Find the answer that would be awarded 3 marks. Choose **A**, **B** or **C**. Explain your choice.

6 There are ten coins in a box.
The value of each coin is shown below.

50p	50p	50p	20p	20p	20p	20p	10p	10p	5p

Vince takes a coin from the box at random and keeps it.
Maria then takes a coin from the box at random and keeps it.

Work out the probability that both Vince and Maria take 20p coins. **(3 marks)**

A: $\frac{4}{10} \times \frac{4}{10} = \frac{16}{100} = \frac{4}{25}$

B: $\frac{4}{10} \times \frac{3}{9} = \frac{12}{90} = \frac{2}{15}$

C: $\frac{4}{10} + \frac{3}{9} = \frac{36}{90} + \frac{30}{90} = \frac{66}{90} = \frac{11}{15}$

Answer B would get 3 marks because the student has understood that after Vince has taken his coin there will be three 20p coins and nine coins in total. They have then correctly multiplied the fractions to find the probability.

Answers

Probability and statistics

Mark the answer

1 Use the mark scheme to assign a mark to the answer. Explain your decision.

3 Jenna recorded the heights, in cm, of 20 shrubs. Show this information in an ordered stem-and-leaf diagram. (3 marks)

42	49	58	36	56	38	50	41	47	63
34	61	45	58	66	39	68	54	43	66

3	6 8 4 9
4	2 9 1 7 5 3
5	8 6 0 8 4
6	3 1 6 8 6

Answer	Notes
3 | 4689 4 | 123579 5 | 04688 6 | 13668	B1 for fully correct unordered or ordered with one error or omission B1 for fully correct ordered stem-and-leaf diagram B1 for key

I would award the answer 1 out of 3 marks because the stem-and-leaf diagram is correct but unordered, and the student has not included a key.

2 Use the mark scheme to assign a mark to the answer. Explain your decision.

6 Here is a list of numbers

5 9 6 10 11 6 7 4 5

(a) Work out the median. (2 marks)

11

Answer	Notes
6	M1 for ordering the 9 numbers A1 cao

I would award the answer 0 out of 2 marks because the student has not ordered the numbers and has just chosen the middle number.

(b) Work out the mean. (2 marks)

$5 + 9 + 6 + 10 + 11 + 6 + 7 + 4 + 5 = 63$

Mean $= 63 \div 9 = 7$

7

Answer	Notes
7	M1 for adding all the numbers and dividing by 9 A1 cao

I would award the answer 2 out of 2 marks because the student has correctly added up all the numbers and divided by 9 to find the mean.

68

Probability and statistics

Re-order the answer

1 Rearrange the working out into the most logical order by numbering each part. One has been done for you.

12 Six numbers are given as 6, 10, 9, 12, 4 and x.

The numbers have a mean of 8

Work out the value of x. (3 marks)

3 $48 - 41$

2 $6 + 10 + 9 + 12 + 4 + x = 41$

4 $x = 7$

1 $6 \times 8 = 48$

2 Rearrange the working out into the most logical order by numbering each part. Use the hint to help.

5 In a large crate there are some apples, some bananas, some oranges and some pears.

Fruit	Apple	Banana	Orange	Pear
Probability	0.28	0.21	$2x$	x

Jeff takes at random a piece of fruit from the crate.

The table shows the probabilities of taking each type of fruit.

The probability that Jeff will take an orange is twice the probability that he will take a pear.

Work out the probability that Jeff will take an orange. (3 marks)

Hint
- The total probability is 1

3 $3x = 0.51$

5 0.17×2

1 $0.28 + 0.21 + 2x + x = 1$

6 $= 0.34$

4 $x = 0.17$

2 $0.49 + 3x = 1$

69

Probability and statistics

Complete the question

1 Use the student's answers and working out to complete the question.

6 There are 200 counters in a bag.

120 of the counters are red.

50 of the counters are blue.

30 of the counters are white.

Raj takes at random a counter from the bag.

Work out the probability that he picks the following.

(a) a red counter (1 mark)

Nailed it!

P(red) $= \frac{3}{5}$ $\frac{3}{5}$

(b) a red or blue counter (2 marks)

Nailed it!

P(red or blue) $= \frac{3}{5} + \frac{1}{4} = \frac{17}{20}$ $\frac{17}{20}$

(c) a white counter (1 mark)

Nailed it!

P(white) $= \frac{3}{20}$ $\frac{3}{20}$

2 Use the student's answer to complete the question.

16 $\mathscr{E}$ = { even numbers less than 24}

A = { 4 , 10 , 14 , 16 , 18 }

B = { 2 , 14 , 18 , 20 }

Complete the Venn diagram to represent this information. (4 marks)

Nailed it!

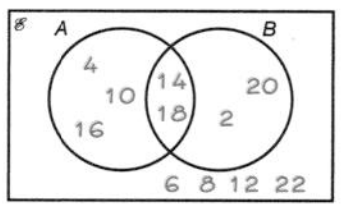

70

Probability and statistics

Complete the answer

1 Use the hint below to complete part (b) of the student's answer so that it would be awarded 3 marks.

19 Lea asked each person in her year group how many cars their family has.

The frequency table shows the results.

Number of cars	0	1	2	3	4
Frequency	7	18	12	9	4

(a) Write down the mode. (1 mark)

1

(b) Work out the mean number of cars. (3 marks)

$(0 \times 7) + (1 \times 18) + (2 \times 12) + (3 \times 9) + (4 \times 4)$

$= 0 + 18 + 24 + 27 + 16 = 85$

Mean $= 85 \div 50 = 1.7$ 1.7

Hint
- First, work out the total number of cars, and the total number of people asked.

2 For each part of the question, complete the student's answer so that it would be awarded full marks.

3 Asha and Pam are in the same class.

The probability that Asha arrives on time is 0.6

The probability that Pam arrives on time is 0.8

(a) Complete the probability tree diagram. (2 marks)

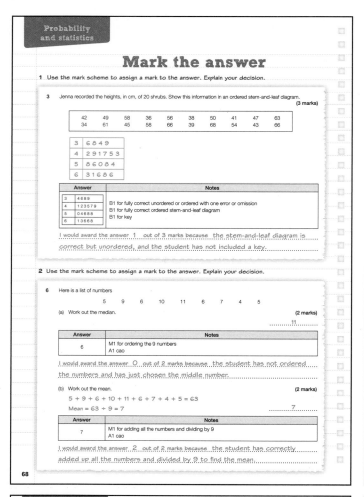

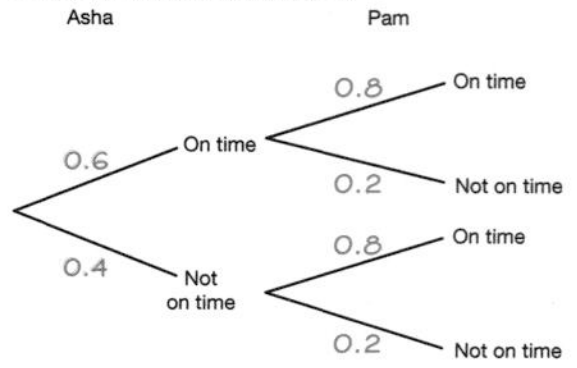

Hint
- Whether Asha is on time does not affect whether Pam is on time – the events are independent.

(b) Work out the probability that they are both on time. (2 marks)

P(Asha on time and Pam on time)

$= 0.6 \times 0.8 = 0.48$ 0.48

Hint
- Read along the branches of the probability tree diagram and multiply.

(c) Work out the probability that only one of Asha or Pam is on time. (2 marks)

P(Asha on time and Pam not on time) or

P(Asha not on time and Pam on time)

$= (0.6 \times 0.2) + (0.4 \times 0.8)$

$= 0.12 + 0.32 = 0.44$ 0.44

Hint
- Add together P(Asha on time and Pam not on time) and P(Asha not on time and Pam on time).

71

Improve the answer

1 For each part of the question, write an improved answer that would be awarded full marks.

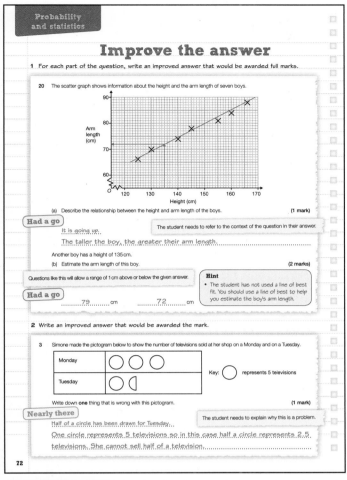

20 The scatter graph shows information about the height and the arm length of seven boys.

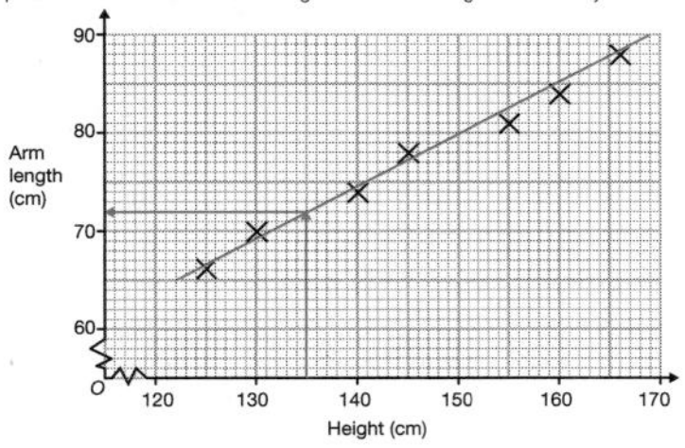

(a) Describe the relationship between the height and arm length of the boys. **(1 mark)**

Had a go

It is going up.

The taller the boy, the greater their arm length.

The student needs to refer to the context of the question in their answer.

Another boy has a height of 135 cm.

(b) Estimate the arm length of this boy. **(2 marks)**

Questions like this will allow a range of 1 cm above or below the given answer.

Hint
• The student has not used a line of best fit. You should use a line of best fit to help you estimate the boy's arm length.

Had a go

79 cm   72 cm

2 Write an improved answer that would be awarded the mark.

3 Simone made the pictogram below to show the number of televisions sold at her shop on a Monday and on a Tuesday.

| Monday | ○ ○ ○ |
| Tuesday | ○ ◗ |

Key: ○ represents 5 televisions

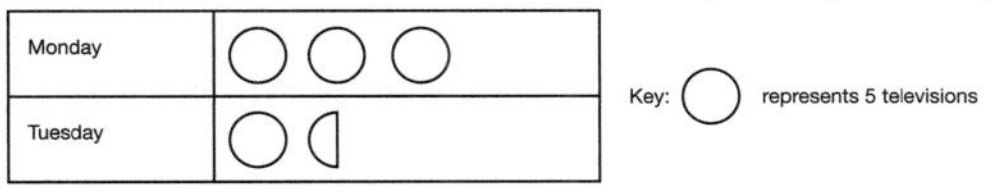

Write down **one** thing that is wrong with this pictogram. **(1 mark)**

Nearly there

Half of a circle has been drawn for Tuesday.

The student needs to explain why this is a problem.

One circle represents 5 televisions so in this case half a circle represents 2.5 televisions. She cannot sell half of a television.

Probability and statistics

Find the answer

1 For each part of the question, find the answer that would be awarded the mark. Choose **A**, **B** or **C**. Explain your choice.

13 Ray rolls an ordinary fair dice.

(a) On the probability scale, mark with a cross (×) the probability that the dice will land on a number greater than 6 **(1 mark)**

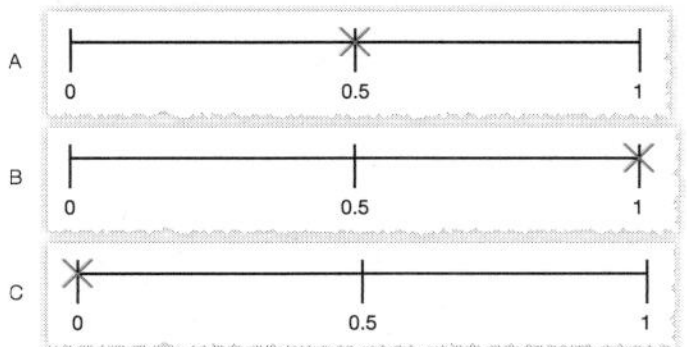

Answer C would get the mark because the student has correctly interpreted the fact that it is impossible for the dice to land on a number greater than 6

(b) On the probability scale, mark with a cross (×) the probability that the dice will land on an odd number. **(1 mark)**

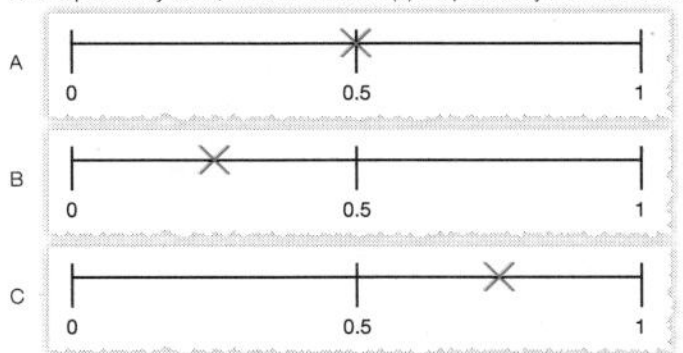

Answer A would get the mark because the student has correctly interpreted that there are three odd numbers out of six.

2 Find the answer that would be awarded the mark. Choose **A**, **B** or **C**. Explain your choice.

8 Here is a fair 6-sided spinner.
Bob is going to spin the spinner once.
Which number is the spinner least likely to land on? **(1 mark)**

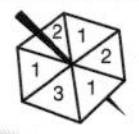

A [1]   B [2]   C [3]

Answer C would get the mark because the student has realised that the number 3 occurs less frequently than either 1 or 2

Probability and statistics

Mark the answer

1 Use the mark scheme to assign a mark to the answer. Explain your decision.

19 Maxine is doing a survey to find out how much time students spend playing on their mobile phones.
She is going to ask the first 10 girls on the register for her form class.
This may **not** produce a good sample for Maxine's survey. Give **two** reasons why. **(2 marks)**

The number of girls she is asking is too small and she is only asking girls.

Answer	Notes
2 correct reasons	B1 for one acceptable reason from bias relating to gender/bias relating to age/bias relating to form class/sample size is too small/sampling is not random B1 for second acceptable reason from bias relating to gender/bias relating to age/bias relating to form class/sample size is too small/sampling is not random

I would award the answer 2 out of 2 marks because the student has correctly stated two acceptable answers.

2 Use the mark scheme to assign a mark to the answer. Explain your decision.

21 The table shows information about annual turnover of a company.

Year	Turnover (£ millions)
2009	17
2010	15
2011	13
2012	10
2013	8
2014	7
2015	5

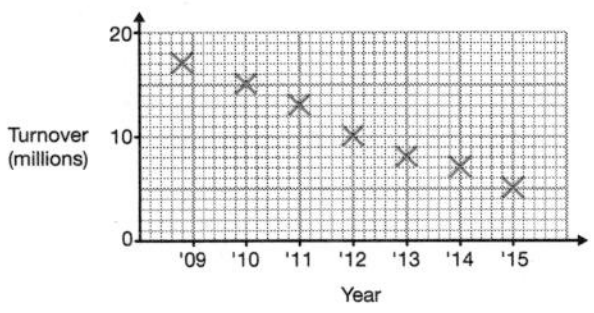

(a) Draw a time series graph to represent this data. **(2 marks)**

Answer	Notes
All points plotted correctly	C1 for at least 5 points plotted correctly C1 for all points plotted correctly (half a square tolerance)

I would award the answer 1 out of 2 marks because the student has plotted 6 points correctly. The first point is more than half a square out of position, so the student loses the final mark.

(b) Write down the type of correlation. **(1 mark)**

Downwards

Answer	Notes
negative	B1 for negative

I would award the answer 0 out of 1 mark because the student has used the wrong terminology to describe the correlation.

Probability and statistics

Improve the answer

1 Write an improved answer that would be awarded 4 marks.

19 Amy asked 40 friends how many minutes they took to get to work.
The table shows her results.

Time taken (t minutes)	Frequency
$0 < t \leq 10$	7
$10 < t \leq 20$	9
$20 < t \leq 30$	12
$30 < t \leq 40$	8
$40 < t \leq 50$	4

Work out an estimate for the mean time taken. **(4 marks)**

Nearly there

$(10 \times 7) + (20 \times 9) + (30 \times 12) + (40 \times 8) + (50 \times 4)$
$= 70 + 180 + 360 + 320 + 200$
Mean $= 1130 \div 40 = 28.25$ 28.25

The student has not used the midpoints to estimate the mean.

$(5 \times 7) + (15 \times 9) + (25 \times 12) + (35 \times 8) + (45 \times 4)$
$= 35 + 135 + 300 + 280 + 180$
Mean $= 930 \div 40 = 23.25$ 23.25

2 Use the hint below to write an improved answer that would be awarded the mark.

12 The pie charts give information about the types of drinks some boys and girls prefer.

Boys   Girls

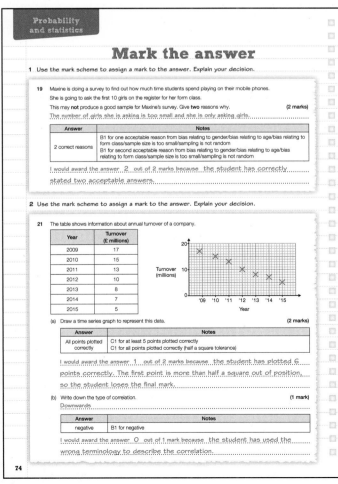

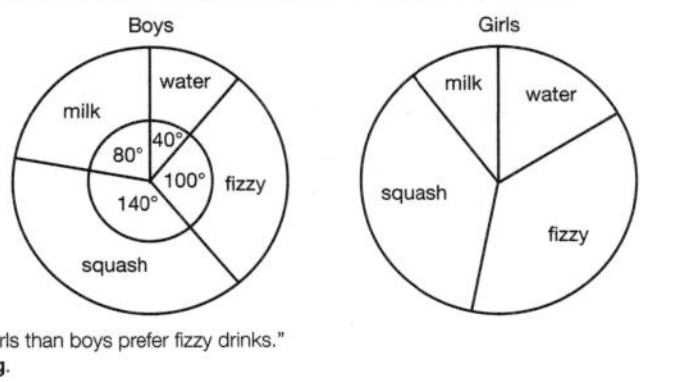

Ang says, "More girls than boys prefer fizzy drinks."
He could be **wrong**.
Explain why. **(1 mark)**

Had a go

The pie chart does not show the angles for the girls.

Hint
• Think about what you would need to know in order to decide whether Ang's statement is true.

We don't know the total number of boys and girls so we can't work out how many of each prefer fizzy drinks.

Published by Pearson Education Limited, 80 Strand, London, WC2R 0RL.

www.pearsonschools.co.uk

Edited, typeset and produced by Elektra Media Ltd

Illustrated by Elektra Media Ltd
Cover illustration by Miriam Sturdee

First published 2018

21 20 19 18
10 9 8 7 6 5 4 3 2 1

British Library Cataloguing in Publication Data

A catalogue record for this book is available from the British Library.

ISBN 978 1 292 23026 9

Copyright notice

Printed in Italy by L.E.G.O. S.p.A

Acknowledgements

We would like to thank Joni Sommerville, Theo Mellors, Emily Plenty, John-Paul Duddy, Emily Atkinson, Jess Salmon, Holly Coop, Matthew Foot and David Birch for their invaluable help in providing student tips for the series.

Note from publisher

1. While the publishers have made every attempt to ensure that advice on the qualification and its assessment is accurate, the official specification and associated assessment guidance materials are the only authoritative source of information and should always be referred to for definitive guidance.

Pearson examiners have not contributed to any sections in this resource relevant to examination papers for which they have responsibility.

2. Pearson has robust editorial processes, including answer and fact checks, to ensure the accuracy of the content in this publication, and every effort is made to ensure this publication is free of errors. We are, however, only human, and occasionally errors do occur. Pearson is not liable for any misunderstandings that arise as a result of errors in this publication, but it is our priority to ensure that the content is accurate. If you spot an error, please do contact us at resourcescorrections@pearson.com so we can make sure it is corrected.